HOOKED

A concise guide to the underlying mechanics of addiction
and treatment for patients, families, and providers

ARWEN PODESTA, MD

ISBN 978-1-952481-31-4
Library of Congress Control Number: 2021911785

Printed in the United States of America
Published in Hellertown, PA
For information or to purchase bulk copies, contact the publisher at
Jennifer@BrightCommunications.net

Bright
COMMUNICATIONS
www.BrightCommunications.net

CONTENTS

FOREWORD

Dr. Arwen Podesta is a rare breed of addiction psychiatrist: Not only is she one of the few US psychiatrists to be board certified in addiction medicine (with extensive practical experience working in one of the most difficult and prevalent areas of addiction in the US) but also she is one of the very few addiction psychiatrists to take a fully integrative approach, which is essential to sustainable sobriety and healing.

Hooked is concise and easy to read, while being full of helpful scientific and practical advice for those with addiction, their families, their friends, and health practitioners. In it, Dr. Podesta deconstructs the disease of addiction, explaining its genetic, neurological, biochemical, psychological, and lifestyle contributors, and how they all interact to create the perfect storm.

She offers us a comprehensive set of biochemical and psychological treatment options and the various schools of thought around them. She shares her own philosophy, which is to treat the whole person, using temporary medication-assisted treatment, if necessary, while she and her team support the biochemical, psychological, and lifestyle interventions which take time but address the root cause of addiction, therefore allowing for long-term sobriety and healing.

With her team at Podesta Wellness, Dr. Podesta treats addiction by working with the patient's biochemistry (genetics and how they affect brain chemistry; epigenetic factors such as nutritional imbalances, gut issues, toxic load, and hormone imbalances; and medication-assisted treatment, when necessary) as well as psycho-spiritual factors (such as stress and trauma) and lifestyle habits and circumstances (such as lack of sleep and inappropriate exercise, but also poverty and incarceration, which are prevalent factors in addiction).

This is reflected in the formula she coined (see opposite page):

Biology + Stress + Drug = Addiction

The prevalence of addiction combined with poor treatment outcomes, makes addiction one of the most pressing public and private health issues. Indeed, since 2009, there has been a 30-percent increase in worldwide drug use, to 269 million drug users in 2018, of which 35 million, or 13 percent, suffer from the disease of addiction. Drug overdose deaths have more than tripled since 1990. And in the US, almost 130 people a day die of an opioid overdose.

The disease of addiction has shown itself to be an intractable one, with relapse rates for most addiction treatment hovering at around 60 to 70 percent. This is perhaps because most addiction treatment does not cover the full spectrum of biochemical, psychological, and lifestyle diagnoses and treatments. Indeed, too few addiction psychiatrists or rehab clinics diagnose and treat an addict's underlying biochemistry in combination with their psychological issues, lifestyle habits, and life circumstances.

Dr. Podesta's approach, outlined in this brilliant book, takes all these into account and demonstrates that the chance of recovery is significantly higher with an integrative approach combining biochemical treatments (natural supplements, medications, diet) with psychotherapy and other somatic therapies, with lifestyle habits and circumstance changes.

Hers is a rare combination of scientific understanding and analysis, extensive medical and practical experience, and compassion wrapped in an accessible, non-judgemental tone, which make this book an absolute gem for addicts, their families, and health practitioners.

Hooked should be required reading for anyone who struggles with addiction or is trying to help those who do.

—Kirkland Newman Smulders

Founder and editor, mindhealth360.com

Host, *The MindHealth360 Show*

AUTHOR'S NOTE

For many years, addiction has been seen and treated as a social disease. Punishment and social treatment were the tenets of treatment. President Nixon started the war on drugs in 1971. With more enforcement, we had more prisoners in jail because of drug addiction, but they were not receiving treatment.

In recent years, the pendulum has started swinging the other way—toward understanding that addiction is indeed a disease of the brain. Furthermore, medical treatment of addiction is effective and preferable to social stigmatization and incarceration.

Many articles and books have been published stating that addiction is not a disease at all, but that it is caused only by severe stress and sometimes childhood problems. Once the stress is dealt with or removed, it is suggested that addiction is gone. This is interesting and, in fact, true for some people. A common story often told is about Vietnam veterans returning from war with addiction. During the Vietnam War, those serving were often offered amphetamines and opioids with the intent of helping soldiers do their jobs, numb them out, and keep them awake during stressful wartimes. Among those Vietnam veterans who returned and self-reported as having addiction problems, about three-quarters of them got better once life, lifestyle, and stressors improved. The conclusion was that if the stressors are removed, then the addiction subsides. But that leaves one-quarter of that cohort still suffering from addiction.

This leads to my simple formula:

For some people, if you remove the stress and the drug, the addiction or dependence and cravings go away, showing that the biology is not strong enough or even present in addiction for them. For others, the genes, epigenetics, and even a background of stress are too strong, and cravings and addiction remain.

OVERVIEW

As of spring 2016, there were three significant changes surrounding the opioid epidemic and treatment. The Centers for Disease Control and Prevention (CDC) published extensive guidelines related to prescribing opioid painkillers, recommending restricting the number of pain pills prescribed, prescribing for fewer days, and assessing the pill misuse risk (Dowell et al., 2016). The American Society of Addiction Medicine released practice guidelines that included giving patients or their family members a prescription for naloxone (Narcan), an opioid overdose rescue kit (American Society of Addiction Medicine, 2016). Naloxone blocks opioid receptors, resulting in the reversal of an overdose.

Some states provide naloxone rescue kits to known opioid users and sometimes to their families. Other states have suggestions to use a naloxone nasal spray rescue. Either way, this could be lifesaving for many patients. Finally, the US Department of Health and Human Services (HHS) suggested that some doctors authorized to prescribe buprenorphine may be able to increase the number of patients from 100 to 275, which will greatly improve access to care. At around the same time, HHS announced the appropriation of around 100 million dollars to increase access to addiction prevention and treatment programs (Substance Abuse and Mental Health Services Administration (SAMHSA), 2016).

In the light of these advances, there was certain to be more treatment options available. With that, patients and their loved ones needed to understand the disease of addiction and avail themselves of different treatment options.

Why Am I Writing This Book?

Addiction is complex, but we understand more and more about causes, complications, and effective treatments. There are many interesting books on the market. Still, very few are concise and answer the questions that my students and my patients and their loved ones ask about addiction: What is it? Why do we care about addiction? Why do some people get addicted? What do we do about it? This book will answer these questions more clearly and simply.

Very few physicians are trained in addiction. I am a board-certified psychiatrist with specialty board certification in addiction medicine. I have studied and worked in this field for more than 15 years. In 2016, there were 5,100 physicians board-certified in addiction. As of 2019, about 6,000 physicians were board-certified in addiction medicine by the American Board of Preventive Medicine, and 1,164 were certified by the American Academy of Addiction Psychiatry. In 2018, more than 164 million Americans aged 12 and older had used substances in the past month, more than 60 percent of the US population (Lipari & Park-Lee, 2019).

Often, providers (MDs, DOs, PAs, NPs) not trained or certified in addiction do not even think to ask about recovery, addiction history, or problems with substances. Yet, the media reports over and over that there is a massive epidemic of addiction, especially narcotics and prescribed medications. Americans comprise less than 5 percent of the world's population but consume 99 percent of the world's hydrocodone supply and 78 percent of the world's oxycodone supply (Downey et al., 2017). According to the US Opioid Dispensing Rate Maps by the CDC, opioid prescription peaked at 81.3 prescriptions per 100 people in 2012. However, this rate declined to 46.7 prescriptions per 100 people in 2019. In some counties, the rate was so high that enough opioid prescriptions were dispensed such that every person in that county could have had a 60-day prescription in their pill cabinet (Centers for

Disease Control and Prevention, National Center for Injury Prevention and Control, 2020).The US leads prescriptions in other classes of medications that can be misused, such as benzodiazepines and stimulants. These medications are usually prescribed by well-meaning providers (and sometimes even other specialists, such as dentists and podiatrists). Still, they are sometimes prescribed to people who misuse or use them in their addiction.

I am writing this book to present the facts and debunk the myths about substance problems and addiction. I am writing this for any audience, from health-care providers to substance treatment counselors to patients suffering from substance problems to loved ones of those who are struggling with the disease of addiction.

Why Do We As a Society Need to Care about Addiction?

More than 70,300 Americans died from a drug-involved overdose in 2019 compared to 38,329 in 2010 (National Institute on Drug Abuse, 2021), with more than 130 people a day dying from opioid-related drug overdoses (Health Resources and Services Administration, 2020).

About 1 out of 10 people will have a serious substance-use problem in his or her lifetime. One in 3 of us is directly affected by addiction, so even if we do not individually suffer from addiction or substance use problems, about a third of us will have a loved one, boss, employee, or friend who does (American Psychiatric Association, 2013). Since 2010, heroin use and overdose have increased in epidemic proportions (Overdose Detection Mapping Application Program, 2020).This has gotten worse, in part, because our medical profession has restricted access to opioid pain pills. And, although the Drug Enforcement Agency has restricted the number of pain pills doctors can write for, there is an increase in prescribing once more. So, bring in street heroin, which is cheaper than pain pills and often easier to get, and tons of people turn to it in lieu of prescriptions.

According to the CDC December 2020 report, more than 57 thousand opioid overdoses occurred between May 2019 and May 2020. That does not include the number of deaths related to other drugs, cocaine, alcohol, and so on (Ahmad et al., 2020). The cost of drug abuse and addiction to society, combining health-care costs, productivity loss, crime, incarceration, and drug-related law enforcement, is close to 740 billion dollars yearly (National Institute on Drug Abuse, 2020).

How Can a Loved One Help?

Addiction is a whole-family problem but not necessarily a family disease, yet it often does have genetic and biological underpinnings (Shafiei et al., 2014). Nonetheless, the family needs to participate in helping to affect a change. Per experts, when families and loved ones are supportive and involved with treatment, there is a marked improvement in the success rate for addiction treatment.

In order to help, family members can follow these simple guidelines:

- Have a decent understanding of addiction and substance use.
- Be loving and supportive but not enabling.
- Seek assistance for yourself (Al-Anon, individual therapy) so that you can stay well while helping the patient get help.

To **enable** refers to the positive act of helping someone accomplish something that could not be done alone. But **enabling** also refers to the act of helping someone in such a way that rather than solving a problem, it is, in fact, being perpetuated.

In this view, enabling behavior is any purposeful action or inaction that allows individuals struggling with addiction to continue their bad habits, without assuming any responsibility for the outcome.

When a spouse covers for a partner who is too hungover to go to work, he or she is enabling that behavior. This not only promotes unhealthy behavior, but it can have dire consequences as well.

What Is Addiction?

Many people experiment with substances, including alcohol, but only some become addicted. Many people who do not become addicted nonetheless have consequences—physical, legal, or other—but they may not be considered addicts. When I speak of people with addiction in this book, I am not talking about those who dabble, experiment, or occasionally use substances—even illegal ones. I am talking about those who have the brain disease of addiction.

The official American Society of Addiction Medicine (ASAM) definition is "a treatable, chronic medical disease involving complex interactions among brain circuits, genetics, the environment, and an individual's life experiences. People with addiction use substances or engage in behaviors that become compulsive and often continue despite harmful consequences" (American Society of Addiction Medicine, 2019).

Active addiction is an imbalance in brain chemistry, starting with a genetic predisposition made susceptible to stress, inflammation, chronic use, and inability to achieve stable chemistry because of chemical depletion. Self-medication to fill a void or treat a physical or mental symptom may result in addiction. This is considered self-medicating gone wrong.

Addiction is not bad people doing bad things. Addiction is not a choice. Addiction is similar to other chronic illnesses, such as heart disease or diabetes, that disrupt the underlying organ's normal, healthy functioning, causing harmful consequences. These diseases are preventable and treatable, but if left untreated, they can relapse and impact people for a lifetime (Smith, 2012).

Simply put, addiction is a chronic, relapsing illness causing impaired control, continued use despite harm, compulsive use, and cravings (Fraser et al., 2014).

Chronic means that it is a long-lasting condition that can be controlled but not cured, like most cases of diabetes.

Percentage of Patients That Relapsed

TYPE I DIABETES
30 TO 50%

DRUG ADDICTION
40 TO 60%

HYPERTENSION
50 TO 70%

ASTHMA
50 TO 70%

Why is Addiction Treatment Evaluated Differently?
(National Institute on Drug Abuse, 2018)

Many diseases have regular relapse or recurrence of the condition after a period of remission. For example, once diagnosed, hypertension has a 50- to 70-percent relapse rate. It is interesting to compare addiction to other chronic relapsing diseases, such as cancer or heart disease. When cancer relapses, we usually blame the medication or the disease and then do an aggressive workup to find better or more-effective treatments to protect the patient from the disease. But, in addiction relapse, we historically blame the patient (National Institute on Drug Abuse, 2018).

Impaired control means the inability to limit an action despite the intention. Related to substances, addiction is the inability to stop consuming.

Continued use is characteristic of addiction, even in the light of legal problems, losing jobs, failing relationships, and even contracting infectious diseases.

Compulsive use means that one is continuing to use repeatedly without it leading to actual pleasure or reward.

Craving is when there is a strong desire for something, either triggered or not. A triggered craving is when you see/smell/hear something that you associate with the substance use, and then you imagine using, and you even get a taste in your mouth for it.

In neuroscience, it is often said that cells that fire together, wire together

(Shatz, 1992, p. 64). Most people can relate to this. For example: Every time I go to a baseball game, I have a hot dog. After a while, every time I think about a baseball game, I think about eating a hot dog. These "wires" in the brain are like electrical circuits, so when you associate one thing with another, the thought circuits fire together. Another example is associating a certain scent, like incense, with your drug dealer. Then, every time you smell that scent, it may fire the neurons related to the drug memories. Non-triggered cravings are from a different part of the brain and are more of an internal, constant craving.

What Do We Do?

There are many types of treatment, with wide ranges of success percentages. It is difficult to get a true sense of success. Definition of success varies, as does the actual reporting of success. Every treatment center that I am aware of has what seems to be a skewed report of success rates, either because unsuccessful people fall out of treatment early or many people are lost to follow-up and are not counted either way.

Twelve-step programs, such as Alcoholics Anonymous (AA) or Narcotics Anonymous (NA), are peer support groups. The success rates when someone uses only 12-step work vary. A 2020 Cochrane Review reports that the "evidence suggests that 42 percent of participants participating in AA would remain completely abstinent one year later, compared to 35 percent of participants receiving other treatments, including CBT (cognitive behavioral therapy) (Kelly et al., 2020, para. 3).

These numbers speak well for success for some. Still, the 58 percent that do not continue abstinence are often at risk for problems, including overdose (Kelly et al., 2020). Some people spontaneously quit with no help at all. There is a pretty low success rate with quitting the substance with no support.

People will have the best success if they go to the level of care appropriate for their needs. Fortunately, the American Society of Addiction Medicine created a set of Placement Criteria guidelines, which can help determine the individual's needs.

- *Therapeutic Community:* A long-term residential treatment center that is group-based and often peer-run. These communities are usually voluntary and may not have medical treatment, although many programs incorporate medical treatment into them. Some are one to two years long, often not covered by insurance.
- *28-Day Residential Treatment:* Usually counselor-driven, with group and individual treatment programs. Many have medical and psychiatric treatments available, but not all.
- *Intensive Outpatient Program (IOP):* Allows the patient to live at home and go to a facility to do individual, group, and family therapy focusing on the addiction. Lasts anywhere from 8 to 12 weeks and usually has a weekly after-care component.

Historically, the success of addiction treatment is low, but the longer the treatment, the better. It is difficult to assess treatment success rates, as there is a lot of loss to follow-up. Also, treatment centers that advertise their rates may have a bias based on self-selection. Typically, it takes many attempts of different ways of treating addiction before one sticks. This is why we have to identify the disease early, have good treatment available, and educate society on this public health crisis!

In a 2015 study comparing more than 650 opioid pain-pill-addicted patients who received medication-assisted treatment (medicine for opioid use disorder; see page 40) for 18 months versus those who were tapered off of pain pills to abstinence, those who continued to receive medicine at the 18-month interview were more than twice as likely to report avoidance of non-medical use of opioids when compared to those who were not; 80 percent versus 36.6 percent (Sarlin, 2015).

In 2003, a pinnacle study was performed, comparing 40 opioid-using patients (heroin) with medication treatment for opioid use versus a placebo over the course of one year. All patients in the placebo group relapsed or dropped out of treatment by two months, and four died. Seventy-five percent of the patients in the medication-treated group remained in the study by one

Four Factors That Influence an Individual's Success

- The individual (especially the individual's brain chemistry based on genetics, biology, and more)
- The addiction (what type of drug)
- Coexisting conditions (Depression, chronic pain, anxiety, and more)
- Psychosocial and family issues (family dynamic problems, socioeconomic, housing, and more.)

year, and none died (Kakko et al., 2003). Ensuing studies reveal similar data; however, placebo is no longer used because it's unethical.

Some of these numbers are promising, but even the best treatments listed on the opposite page have a 25-percent fail rate. If I were a mom worried about a potential overdose and death, I would not feel comforted by those rates. The overall outcome can be improved by understanding the specifics of the sickness and the individuals who suffer from it.

Remember, addiction is a brain disease, not a lack of willpower and not poor judgment (Garbely, 2017). It is a very intertwined brain chemistry problem. For many people, the drug causes brain changes that make it think that the drug will fix the changes, but, in truth, the drug makes the changes worse. Addiction hijacks the intellectual brain. It can be so strong that even the smartest person can easily succumb to its powers. A patient in early treatment relapsed on heroin after a dealer called her, and to entice her to come over and use, he told her, "This shit is so good, two people died on it last week." Even though the patient is intelligent, her disease hijacked her intellectual brain, and she went over and used the deadly heroin. Luckily, she did not die—that time.

BIOLOGY OF ADDICTION

Neurochemistry Basics

Here are the basic components of the brain. The brain is an organ that is made up of functional cells that are known as neurons. Neurons communicate with each other by neurotransmitters, also known as chemical messengers. Examples of neurotransmitters include dopamine, serotonin, gamma amino-butyric acid (GABA), glutamate, and enkephalins. These chemical messengers send signals that affect our thoughts and feelings.

Dopamine is the alarm, causing wakefulness, focus, reward, and pleasure. Serotonin is related to mood, memory, mental well-being, cognition, and sleep. GABA and glutamate are opposites, working to balance each other.—GABA calming and dampening anxiety and glutamate causing excitation. Enkephalins are the brain's natural opioids, which give pleasure and reward, alleviate pain, and more.

The most important neurotransmitters when it comes to addiction are dopamine, serotonin, GABA, and glutamate.

Neurons are organized into networks or circuits to carry out specific functions or behaviors. Three areas are often discussed in addiction, which are the dorsolateral prefrontal cortex (DLPC), the nucleus accumbens (NA), and the ventral tegmentum (VTM). They are directly linked by main networks, or circuits, and facilitate decision making, social behavior, planning, and general executive functioning.

Dopamine Tone: We want the right amount of dopamine balanced in the right location. Dopamine tone is a way to describe that. Rat studies have shown that unhealthy dopamine activity is akin to unhealthy reward seeking. Many colleagues equate this to hedonic tone.

Hedonic Tone: An inherent set-point for the ability to experience reward, "the trait or genetic predisposition underlying one's baseline range and lifelong characteristic ability to feel pleasure" (Sternat & Katzman, 2016, p.2150). In those with low hedonic tone, neural pathways and chemicals are thought to be disrupted.

The DLPC's primary function is judgment, and it controls the NA. The NA is mainly involved with motivation, and VTM produces the chemical messenger of dopamine in the setting of stimuli or cues. The NA and VTM are often known as the pleasure-reward center.

In addiction or the chronic misuse of a substance, the chemical messenger, dopamine, is out of balance in a needed area and causes a change in how the circuits are supposed to function, particularly the reward circuit, and reinforce substance use also known as neuroadaptation (Lovinger, 2012). There are natural pleasures in life in which all five senses provide input. Finding rewards in life establishes habits that dominate our behaviors. The reward is signaled by dopamine release. Eating chocolate, exercising, having orgasms, being kind—and using drugs—elevate dopamine. After the dopamine spike, sometimes, depending on the substance, there is a dopamine drop, leading to empty and negative feelings. That is followed by the quest to resolve the negative feelings and feel good again or to maintain the dopamine baseline for functioning.

An example of how it functions is: There is a trigger or cue followed by a perception or being aware, their imagining the future with the substance of behavior with a subsequent release of dopamine from the VTM with an activation of the NA with a craving that then communicates with the VTM for more dopamine and the DLPC starts to plan on how to get or fulfill the craving.

Once the craving has been satisfied, then there is a feeling of relief, but quickly after, there are feelings of shame and guilt that then activate the VTM to produce and release dopamine to restart the cycle. The circuits' inappropriate working pathway is often referred to as the addiction cycle, which is broken up into three stages: 1) binge-intoxication, 2) negative affect and withdrawal, and 3) preoccupation and craving.

The neuroadapted (or addicted) brain has a problem resetting the circuit or network to work back to its baseline functioning. The non-neuroadapted brain, when getting a dopamine reward with a drug, chocolate, orgasm, and the like, experiences a reward or euphoria. Still, each circuit acts as a checks-and-balance for the other.

The only way the individual with addiction can get close to feeling normal again is to keep using the drug. This is what he struggles with daily—to feel like he is surviving. It becomes a survival drive to use, like hunger, thirst, sleep, or even breathing.

Neurobiology of Addiction

Everything we ingest, do, feel, and think affects our brain chemistry. In turn, our brain chemistry affects everything we ingest, do, feel, and think. The chemicals that send the signals that affect our thoughts and feelings are neurotransmitters. As noted in the section above, the most important neurotransmitters when it comes to addiction are dopamine, serotonin, GABA, and glutamate.

The brain is the most complex organ to treat because, unlike the heart, liver, or pancreas, doing the healthy thing for this organ is controlled by the organ itself. It is like if you had both hands injured and the only way you could put salve on the injuries was with your hands, but they are both too injured to do so.

In the brain's deep center lies the midbrain, where the pleasure centers and reward pathways exist. The pleasure-reward center consists of the ventral tegmentum (VT) and the nucleus accumbens (NA), which are directly linked to the frontal lobe (specifically the prefrontal and frontal cortex), where decision making, social behavior, planning, and general executive functioning are carried out.

Chemical signals of neurotransmitters, especially dopamine and serotonin, are sent from the VT to the NA; more chemical signals of the same and other neurotransmitters follow those to the frontal lobe (Little et al., 2013).

The dopamine pathways are responsible for reward and pleasure, fine-motor function, motivation, focus, and control of compulsion and impulsivity. The serotonin pathways affect mood, memory, sleep, cognitive functioning, and an overall sense of well-being.

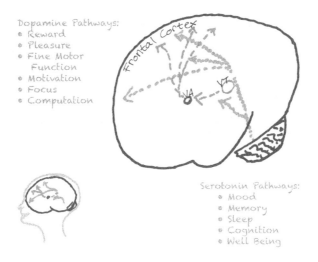

Dopamine Pathways:
- Reward
- Pleasure
- Fine Motor Function
- Motivation
- Focus
- Computation

Serotonin Pathways:
- Mood
- Memory
- Sleep
- Cognition
- Well Being

In these important parts of the brain, the VT and NA, there are receptors for all the neurotransmitters. I like to imagine the receptors as being a chemical baseball glove for the chemicals, and then, after they are caught, other chemical signals are sent and caught at the next step. The brain is a complex system, and each small part is also complex, so an analogy of a single baseball game will not do. With 86 billion neurons in the brain and each neuron having 1 thousand to 10 thousand synapses or ways to communicate with neighboring cells, this baseball analogy is too basic. So, I imagine that there are not multiple baseball games on the same field but thousands, all of them overlapping.

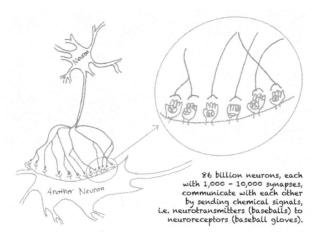

86 billion neurons, each with 1,000 – 10,000 synapses, communicate with each other by sending chemical signals, i.e. neurotransmitters (baseballs) to neuroreceptors (baseball gloves).

In this area, there are receptors for serotonin, glutamate, GABA, endocannabinoids, and nicotine. It is not just our natural chemicals that work at these receptors, but drugs act at these receptors, as well, causing some sort of reward. This depicts the VT's and NA's more detailed view, with their receptors and what drugs work where.

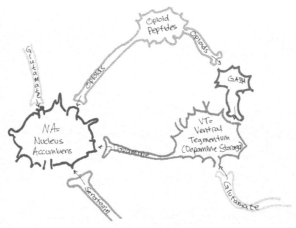

This image shows where different drugs work in the reward cycle in the brain.

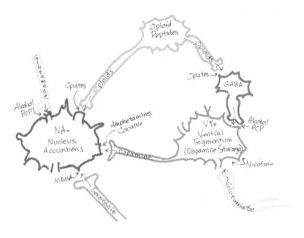

Primer on Genetics and Epigenetics

You are born with a set of genes—half from your mother and half from your father. It is like a house blueprint by an architect. Many aspects are set in stone; eye color and blood type are good examples. Like in the blueprint, the front door's location and the number of stories are for certain. Many outcomes are related to the environment and the materials, such as how the genes fold and make proteins and if the right nutrients and building blocks are available. In the house analogy, what type of siding and flooring and whether the land is arid or wet will determine how the house looks, feels, and functions.

In people, our levels of stress and chaos influence the proteins made. While young, trauma, neglect and abuse, peer influences, general health, and nutrition all determine how the genes fold to make proteins. Epigenetics is how the environment changes the genetic outcome to make someone more or less susceptible to their genetic blueprint (Nestler, 2014).

For example, no matter what I eat, think, or do, my eye color or blood type will not change. But imagine a set of twins with the same gene that predisposes them to a certain type of cancer. Sometimes both will develop it, sadly. But, sometimes, despite the same genes, if one has different stress levels, toxin exposure, nutrition, and overall healthy habits, it may make one more likely to develop cancer than the other.

Epigenetics is responsible for this. There are experts in the field of epigenetics that say that about 60 percent of your health-related genes can be expressed differently by different intake and lifestyle (Alegría-Torres et al., 2011).

In addiction, characteristics of the drug itself can also interact with biological and environmental risk factors to influence addiction development. For example, early substance use is an indicator of problems ahead, including addiction. Also, the route of use of a substance influences the likelihood of addiction; injecting a drug means a higher risk of quickly becoming addicted to that drug than snorting or oral use (Strang et al., 1998).

We know that a chaotic life and stress can influence addiction. Many people turn to alcohol and other drugs during their most stressful times, and they develop an addiction. Think of how many people you may know who have been relatively normal social drinkers, and then a divorce, job loss, or natural disaster occurs. They end up drinking heavily, even pathologically, and unable to quit on their own. And, then, when stressors resolve, some of them can return to social nonpathological drinking. Others cannot.

An excellent study in 2002 showed that monkeys with a lower social standing, when faced with stress, would choose cocaine over food (Morgan et al., 2002). But dominant monkeys with the same stressors had fewer brain changes of stress and anxiety and were less likely to choose cocaine.

This is related to how the dopamine receptors change their activity due to epigenetics caused by being nondominant. This behavior directly correlates to someone suffering from domestically violent relationships, bullying, or poor parenting and their increased susceptibility to drug use.

Why Do People Have a Drug of Choice?

Among my colleagues, we commonly use the words *drug of choice*, abbreviated DOC. I would prefer that the term be the *most effective reward* (MER), getting away from the archaic idea that addiction is a choice and that the drug is the reason for the addiction. One person may positively respond to or get a high dopamine spike with a different drug than someone else. Some people get paranoid and panicky on uppers, others feel normal, and still others get focused and calm. This is due to the underlying neurochemistry and which neurotransmitter system might be needier or have variants. Here is a simplistic breakdown of how the brain's chemistry is directly affected by each type of common drug of abuse. All result in a dopamine spike (see the table on page 81).

- Alcohol, amphetamines, and cocaine directly boost dopamine release.
- Serotonin is modulated by LSD, alcohol, and ecstasy (MDMA).
- Opioids and alcohol increase endorphins.
- Alcohol, benzodiazepines, and marijuana modulate GABA.
- Glutamate is modulated by alcohol.
- Endocannabinoids are affected by marijuana.

One person might have something in his genes and brain chemistry that makes the endorphin system more susceptible, and that person may take to opioids, getting enjoyment, feeling energized, or feeling "normal" the first time he tries it. Another person with different genetics will have an adverse effect, such as falling asleep or getting ill. This is true of all other dopamine releasing drugs, which is how the most effective reward is established.

Why Isn't Everyone Who Tries Drugs Addicted?

We know that addiction is not a choice. But experimenting usually is a choice. Many animals seek intoxicants—bison, bees, horses, monkeys, and wallabies. Wallabies are known to jump into poppy fields, flail around in circles, and continue to take in opioids and forego eating and even starve their babies (Crew, 2015). But, not all wallabies do that. Even in a population of wallabies near poppy fields, most will not get so addicted to the poppy opioids that they hurt themselves and their families. But some do. This is the same with

Epigenetics: The change in genetic expression that can be influenced by the environment. This is a natural occurrence. Environment can influence how a gene turns on or off, how a gene transcribes to messenger RNA (mRNA), and how mRNA translates into a protein. Also, the environment can affect how a protein folds to act or not act at its necessary location. Age, lifestyle, nutrition, and disease state can have a profound influence on epigenetics. Epigenetic change can manifest in simple and common changes, such as turning on or off a gene for hair growth. Epigenetics can have serious effects resulting in diseases like cancer, diabetes, depression, or addiction.

humans. It takes the perfect storm of genetics, epigenetics, environment, and drug use to cause the brain to become dependent or addicted.

No single factor determines whether a person will become addicted, although, if someone forced certain drugs onto a person, that person would very likely become addicted. I have worked with several young women who had no genetic predisposition to addiction but were forced into it under the worst circumstances. In the sex- and human-trafficking world, young women are sometimes kidnapped and forced to use drugs, such as cocaine and heroin, and then are raped and sold.

Several of the women I have treated came from chaotic homes with early sexual abuse. The perpetrator would drug and then rape his victim. The victim would become drug-addicted and sometimes persuaded to continue sexual abuse because of the drugs' induced cravings. This is a horrible but powerful story, showing that under the worst circumstances, people can become addicted against their will. One of those victims is now getting her master's degree so she can work to prevent this from happening to other girls and women.

The environment is one factor in addiction, trauma being highly implicated. Also, genetics plays a very significant role. Addiction often runs in families. Some people inherit an opioid receptor gene that makes them more susceptible to euphoria and energy when taking opioids. Some people inherit a gene that decreases the amount of dopamine and serotonin production, so they have low amounts their whole lives until they find a drug that gives them increases (Dreher et al., 2009; Heitland et al., 2012). There are at least 400 locations in the human genome and at least 566 total variants at these locations that influence alcohol use and smoking (National Institute on Drug Abuse, 2019). Genetic research shows that many genes are related to the development of addiction. As we learn more in decades to come, we may be able to actually target treatment based on that genetic knowledge (Downs et al., 2019).

TREATMENTS FOR ADDICTION

Overview of Treatment

There are many types of treatment, and they have varying efficacy and success. You may have heard about smoking cessation and that a combination of treatments is more effective when used together than a singular treatment. The studies show that Chantix (varenicline) plus nicotine replacement (the patch or gum) have greater than 15 percent better outcomes of continued abstinence at three and six months compared with no treatment (Koegelenberg et al., 2014). And adding a peer support group further increases success rates.

In all addiction treatment, applying all tools is the best approach. This could include therapy, peer support, family therapy, medication treatment, or treatment for co-occurring problems, from depression to lack of childcare to legal issues. Some evidence-based therapy types for addiction include motivational enhancement, matrix model, cognitive behavioral therapy, family behavioral therapy, mutual help group, and 12-step (see page 35). When each is used alone, it tends to stay below the 30- to 40-percent success rate in a controlled environment. But, when used together, brain changes occur, and treatments help with continued abstinence, long-term stability, and overall improved health. When medication and therapy are added to abstinence in criminal justice settings such as jail, re-entry court, drug court, and diversion programs, success rates at least double.

The essence of treating addiction is treating all parts of the following equation:

Risk of Abuse / Addiction

Treatment can be broken down in many ways. Here is an overview:

- Mental and physical health
- Synapse/brain recovery
- Stress recovery
- Life skills and recovery tools
- Abstinence

Two regions of the brain are affected by addiction, and comprehensive treatment must target both areas. The frontal lobe, where decision making, thinking, reasoning, and learning occurs, is greatly affected by counseling and therapy. Therapy changes brain chemistry and biology. Therapy and shared experiences, such as group therapy and peer support, increase serotonin in the frontal lobe (Cachia, 2020). Feeling alone decreases serotonin and dopamine tone (see "Dopamine Tone" on page 19), but being with others increases it. Dopamine tone is increased when someone finds purpose in life, has a daily routine, helps others, and practices meditation and gratitude. All of these help the person feel better by stabilizing the chemistry in the brain.

Some people do fine with behavioral interventions alone, whether it be peer-support like a 12-step program or counseling. Many people that I have met have spent years in sobriety with Alcoholics Anonymous but felt that they were white-knuckling it—feeling empty, disconnected, and discontent, but SOBER!

Some people identify with the joking acronym of SOBER: Son Of a Bitch, Everything's Real. Once abstinent, the stressors become more evident,

SOBER: Son Of a Bitch, Everything's Real!

- The bills I've been avoiding have been adding up.
- My car still needs repaired.
- I need to get my teeth fixed; I've been too high to notice the pain.
- I need a job.

And the list goes on. . . .

and people often get overwhelmed, frantically trying to deal with them. The overwhelming feelings decrease mental stability, decreasing dopamine tone and predisposing an addict to relapse.

The part of the brain responsible for those feelings is the part with the reward system in it—the midbrain, which houses the nucleus accumbens and ventral tegmentum. Also affected is the nearby limbic region, which deals with emotion. Treatment here requires some chemical intervention, from Western medication and pharmacotherapy to nutritional and herbal supplementation, or both.

Is Medication Necessary?

Medication is part of the toolbox to treat chronic addiction. There are still holdouts who are completely anti-medication, believing that any medicine is bad. A common objection is that "you're just swapping one addiction for another" when you start taking medications. The most well-known and one of the oldest treatment facilities in the United States, Hazelden Betty Ford, was once opposed to medication management of addiction. In 2012, they publicly endorsed medication-assisted treatment (MAT) for addiction, and similar positions are being adopted by treatment settings across the country (Szalavitz, 2012). For example, we now understand that depression is a brain disease and that some people may need antidepressants.

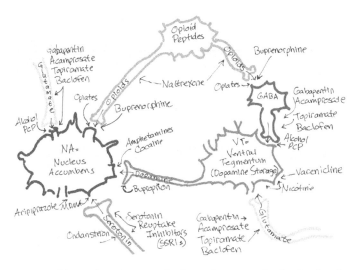

This image adds to the picture of where drugs act in the brain, showing that prescribed medications work in similar locations, but in a more controlled and smooth fashion, without the spikes and dips from the drug.

I have a mid–30s male patient, a father, who was using heroin for about 10 years. During this time, he experienced a downward spiral: He lost his job, got

Medication-Assisted Treatment (MAT)

There are many medicines available and many reasons to use medicine to treat the addiction spectrum. There is acute treatment of withdrawal, or detox, especially when people are coming off alcohol, benzodiazepines, or opioids. There is treatment for psychiatric symptoms associated with substance use and withdrawal, such as anxiety, panic, depression, sleep issues, and mood irritability. There is medication management for reducing cravings and urges. There is medication that blocks the ability to have a response to the substance of abuse. Finally, substitution therapy can fall into all of these categories. See Chapter 4 for more detailed information on medications for addiction.

divorced, lost custody of his children, and lost his house. After detoxification, rehabilitation, 12-step therapy, and an opioid replacement (buprenorphine), he began to get his life back and feel normal. After four months of treatment, he had an apartment and a job, and he started visitation with his children. He lost contact with the doctor who had been prescribing buprenorphine, and he was unable to get the medication for a month. He immediately relapsed and started slipping down the previous path. His addiction hijacked all the tools he had learned. After several months, his job and child visitations were threatened. Through some searching, he found me.

I restarted buprenorphine and helped him get back with his sponsor. He has been stable on medication for more than two years, remained abstinent, is in 12-step recovery, has a job and apartment, and is arranging custody of his children.

Medication management of addiction is not swapping one addiction for another, and it is not harm reduction. It is treatment. It changes the brain chemistry, allowing the dopamine receptors and synapses to regrow and get balanced.

Many physicians and medical providers have different training and differing philosophies on treating addiction. Some do not want to start medication until the patient is completely abstinent for a time. This can prove challenging because the brain is requesting the drug, and the person is miserable until the brain gets its reward. Medications can help provide the reward, albeit more slowly and less strongly, so that the patient can start to make cognitive and lifestyle changes. As opposed to treating other organs, the brain is more complex, as it is the organ that tells us what to do. So if it is broken, it might tell us to do the wrong thing. Therefore, medications can be beneficial, even in early treatment.

Medications are highly effective and have excellent evidence, but they must be used sparingly and only when needed. They are part of the toolbox; they help treat symptoms to help the patient stay in recovery and learn tools for long-term wellness. Some medications may be long term, but most will be short to medium term, while neural growth (neurogenesis), neuron communication (synaptogenesis), and neural repair occur, especially in the first three to six months of recovery.

My philosophy involves stabilizing the addiction until the foundation is built and then moving away from medications, when possible. Sometimes that may take a few months, sometimes much longer. There are, however, some medications that may be indicated for long-term maintenance in some patients.

Types of Treatment Levels and Facilities

Finding the right treatment can be overwhelming. Most programs will report excellent outcomes, but the data can often be skewed. It is essential to understand each type of treatment and then figure out what level is best.

Most people with opioid, alcohol, or benzodiazepines, such as Xanax, Ativan, or Valium, dependence benefit from detoxification, although many people suffer through detoxification independently.

Detoxification Treatments

Hospital-based detoxification is for the patient going through severe opioid, alcohol, or benzodiazepine withdrawal and needs medications with 24-hour nursing care and possibly intravenous and emergency medications. The stay is usually five to seven days and includes evaluations by a physician, a counselor or social worker, and sometimes a psychologist. The patient will receive comfort medications and sometimes replacement medications. During the stay, there are usually some group and individual therapy sessions to start the recovery process and determine the best place to refer after the detox is completed.

Medically assisted detoxification, or *ambulatory detox,* is very similar, except it is usually in a stand-alone, non-hospital facility. Oral medications are used to treat withdrawal symptoms. They are usually affiliated with a residential treatment program facility.

Ambulatory/outpatient detoxification is best for a reliable patient who has a good support system at home and does not need 24-hour nursing. A patient goes to a doctor's office, either outpatient or intensive outpatient program (see opposite page), and is evaluated. A prescription for medications is given, with very clear instructions. Often, the physician or nurse will instruct the pharmacy to fill only one day or a few days' worth at a time, and the patient will have to report back to the office frequently to monitor any symptoms and evaluate other needs. Some programs have a nurse hotline that the patient is to call at certain intervals.

Rehabilitation Programs

Rehabilitation programs come in different levels of care and are based on need. A rehabilitation program is appropriate for someone who is not detoxing or having withdrawal symptoms and is not intoxicated from any drug. A patient will either self-detoxify at home or come from a detox facility. A patient taking cocaine, marijuana, or amphetamines (but not alcohol, benzodiazepines, or opioids) can come to rehabilitation ready to stop using; the patient will not usually need a detox facility.

Residential rehabilitation varies widely in approach, philosophy, style, and quality. They all tend to be at least 21 days of treatment in a place with lodging, and they tend to include activities throughout the day and into the evening as part of the recovery. They are designed for patients who cannot prioritize getting themselves to outpatient treatment and for those who have a toxic or dangerous living environment that influences their relapse risk. Residential rehabs have individual and group sessions to help patients gain life skills and promote relapse prevention, and they often have consulting psychiatrists and primary-care providers on-site. The patient may be able to stay 90 days to six months, depending on several things, including how the program is funded.

Partial hospitalization is usually a four- to eight-week program (that can be extended) in which the patient lives at home but goes to a facility three to five days a week, four to six hours a day. Treatment is in a group or individual setting. Some partial hospitalization programs have medical and psychiatric consultants on-site. Although the patient is living at home during this time, most programs require that they do not work.

Intensive outpatient programs (IOPs) are office-based 9- to 12-hour a week programs, three to four days a week. These are very similar to partial hospitalizations but are fewer hours per week and are slightly less intensive. Many programs allow patients to work and have IOP hours in the evening for convenience.

Outpatient/office treatment is successful for many people who have good social support, have some relapse-prevention skills, and prioritize coming to appointments and meetings. Often, an addiction physician and counselor will work together. The physician prescribes medications, and the counselor sees the patient one to three times a week for skill-building, craving reduction, and further relapse prevention. During counseling, deeper needs are uncovered and addressed, such as anxiety, post-traumatic stress, depression, and more.

Twelve-step/peer groups alone are successful for many people with addiction, as millions have widely used them throughout the last 80 years. If someone with addiction tries this route and is unsuccessful, then a higher treatment level may be indicated.

The cost for all of these services varies widely (except 12-step or peer groups, which are free). Insurance often pays for some or all of the cost. If a patient has no funding, some states have facilities that are available to them. For private pay, with or without insurance, the cost can range from a few thousand dollars up to $80,000 a month.

Higher cost does not necessarily mean better treatment outcomes. Currently, there is no official rating system for ranking the best drug-and-alcohol centers. Some questions that may clarify the level of care needed and the type of facility that would be best are below. There are no right or wrong answers, but the responses will help determine what facility would be best for you or your loved one.

Finding the Right Treatment Program

What is the cost, and how much does insurance cover? Many private facilities are considered out of network. They will tell you that they do not accept your insurance but will often help you file to get reimbursed. Ask them what their typical result is with your insurance. Most will say 60- to 95-percent reimbursement. But remember, the fee must be paid up front, and insurance filing and reimbursement may take months. Staff will be able to let you know their experience, but it will vary with each case.

Does the staff have expertise in treating the patient's addiction? Some are excellent at treating alcohol but not opioids, some are specific for gambling, eating disorders, or any combination.

Is the director a physician, therapist, or PhD? Is that person board certified as an addiction professional? The American Board of Preventative Medicine, Addiction Training (ABPM) or the American Academy of Addiction Psychiatry (AAAP) are the top-line training and certification programs in addiction for physicians. There are also specialty certifications in addiction treatment for PhDs and therapists.

Borderline personality is characterized by emotional instability, impulsivity, and unstable relationships, self-image, and behaviors starting before the age of 18 that are consistent and pervasive. Often, people with borderline personality will say that they have mood swings, but this is different from bipolar disorder, in that borderline mood swings are reactive and momentary. Many with borderline personality have intense fear of abandonment and intense anger. Often, they self-harm. Very often, substance use is present.

Stress and trauma (and especially sexual abuse) experienced as a youngster is highly correlated to borderline personality. Also, genetics and brain structure, as well as hormones, are involved in the development of the disorder.

Psychotherapy is the most effective treatment for borderline personality. Dialectal behavioral therapy (DBT), both group and individual, is the current choice model for treatment.

Do they provide individualized treatment plans? Most places will say that they do not use a cookie-cutter, one-size-fits-all treatment approach. Ask what some of the differences are.

Is the facility based on 12-step? Many patients will thrive with this style, but many do better with mixed or non-12-step.

What sort of counseling is provided? Cognitive-behavioral therapy (CBT) helps manage symptoms related to addiction, anxiety, depression, and post-traumatic stress. Dialectical behavioral therapy (DBT) is excellent for patients who have difficulty regulating emotions and behavior and may have borderline personality traits.

What other activities are available? Some have luxurious activities, such as massage, horseback riding, or yoga, that may help the patient feel more involved and relaxed.

Does the facility offer psychiatric consultation and addiction medicine as part of treatment? Nutrition consultation? General medicine? Functional medicine? Depending on the patient's level of need or interest in including medical wellness as part of treatment, knowing what is available can be helpful.

Treatment Goals

Many people in abstinence-based recovery are adamant that anything less than abstinence is not recovery. But what is a successful treatment? Is it abstinence? Recovery? Healthy lifestyle? Staying alive? Staying out of jail? Contributing to society?

I worked with a young adult female patient who was putting herself through private college by working as an exotic dancer. She found that she could ignore the anxiety and distaste for the work when she used alcohol and cocaine. When she was sober, she felt traumatized and horrified by her work. Nevertheless, she had committed herself to just one more year to finish her degree from this prestigious school.

The school began requiring random drug testing, and she came up positive for cocaine. She decided to stop using cold turkey and had no physical withdrawal. But, she once again suffered from the symptoms that she had been self-medicating. She came to me to try to feel better. We started some medication for mood and post-traumatic stress and also individual therapy focusing on trauma treatment.

After several months, she was not using cocaine and was doing well in school. She was still drinking, but less so. Some would suggest that she did not have a successful outcome. She had, however, met her treatment goals and was working toward success on multiple levels.

The patients I see have a variety of definitions of success. My goal is always to help patients find mental and physical wellness and feel stable and productive. This may include many stages of treatment and many different needs. For some, it will require abstinence-based recovery—no alcohol, and no other intoxicants. For some, it may mean being free of the drug that they came to me to stop using, usually opioids, but perhaps continuing to drink socially, for example. And for many, it will mean finding a healthy, balanced lifestyle, perhaps with prescribed medication, to assist in treatment and wellness.

A patient I will call Sally was using heroin and pain pills on and off for many years. During that time, she lost her job, had a broken marriage, and lost privileges to visit her children. She went into inpatient recovery for 30 days and 60 days a few times and, when released, was not on any medications. She relapsed shortly after leaving each time. Eventually, she began seeing me for addiction medication as an outpatient. For the last few years, she has not used illicit drugs, and most important, she has a steady job and a relationship with her children. She is taking buprenorphine and is seeing a therapist weekly but is not in a 12-step recovery program. Sally has met her goals, and therefore, she is successful.

As a treatment provider, I look at successes in increments, one day at a time. At each interval, from one week to one month to six months to one year and beyond, I reevaluate the treatment goals and overall plan with the patient and family. When I start a medication, I want to see three to six months of improving stability before changing or stopping that medication. It will take at least that long to observe the effects of brain chemistry changes and new patterns in behavior to emerge.

MEDICATIONS FOR ADDICTION

Medications for Nicotine Dependence

FDA approved in adults:

Nicotine-replacement therapies—Delivered through patch, gum, lozenge, inhaler, these can help change the physical habit of smoking but still provide nicotine to the system.

Bupropion (Zyban, Wellbutrin)—This is an antidepressant that increases dopamine in the system. It is very effective in smoking cessation because people get hooked on nicotine because of the dopamine reward cycle.

Varenicline (Chantix)—This is a partial nicotine receptor agonist, so it partially blocks the nicotine receptor, thereby making nicotine unable to bind and stimulate the dopamine reward cycle.

Not FDA approved:

Nortriptyline

Clonidine

L-methylfolate—(medical foods: Enlyte, EnbraceHR, Deplin; or over-the counter formulations at lower doses)—This activated B vitamin increases dopamine, serotonin, and norepinephrine production in some people, and therefore helps stabilize dopamine tone (see "Dopamine Tone" on page 19) (Alphasigma, 2019).

Medications for Alcohol Dependence

FDA approved in adults:

Disulfiram (Antabuse)—This medicine is always provided along with therapy. The patient must take it daily to get the best effects. While on this medication, if someone drinks alcohol, it will cause a reaction that includes headache, nausea, and a hangover feeling, called acute ethanol toxicity.

Naltrexone (ReVia, Vivitrol)—This medication is approved for the treatment of alcohol and helps prevent the "do it again" (repeating desire) of excessive drinking and helps reduce cravings and the number of drinking days. The intramuscular injection form of this medicine (Vivitrol) is given monthly (in place of the daily pill form) for increased adherence and compliance. It has the added benefit of removing the habit of taking something daily.

Acamprosate (Campral)—This is often used for cravings and somewhat for anxiety that comes with cravings.

Not FDA approved (used off-label):

Topiramate (Topamax)—An antiepileptic and migraine medication that is also used to treat bipolar disorder.

Ondansetron (Zofran)—An antinausea medication that works by modulating serotonin.

Baclofen—An anti-muscle-spasm medication that regulates dopamine impulses in the brain.

Ketamine—An N-methyl-D-aspartic acid (NMDA) antagonist, traditionally used as an anesthetic (Sleigh et al., 2014).

Medications for Opioid Dependence

All of the following are FDA approved:

Naltrexone (ReVia, Vivitrol)—Naltrexone is an oral opioid blocker used to effectively prevent feeling the effects of opioids, thereby causing no reward. This extinguishes the opioid reward-pleasure cycle, which disconnects the patient's association of opioids and pleasure and decreases cravings. Vivitrol is the intramuscular injection form of this medicine that is given on a monthly basis (in place of the daily pill form) for increased adherence and compliance. It has the added benefit of removing the habit of taking something daily.

Methadone— This is a full-acting synthetic opioid that is quickly absorbed and has a long half-life. It has been used for the treatment of opioid addiction

Half-life: All medications and toxins (drugs) have half-lives. Half-life describes the amount of time the substance (medication or drug) takes to metabolize and excrete, by the liver or kidney, to a decreased level by half.

since 1947. Methadone treatment for addiction requires regular (initially daily) visits to a methadone clinic for administration and counseling (Tadros et al., 2020).

Buprenorphine (Subutex, Suboxone, Zubsolv, Sublocade)—In contrast to methadone, buprenorphine is a partial opioid agonist, meaning that it turns on and turns off the receptors, creating a ceiling effect. Hence, the brain is not fully activated by the opioid. It is touted as being safer and having lower abuse potential than methadone. Buprenorphine has been FDA approved since 2002. It can be prescribed in a regular outpatient clinic setting.

Medications for Cocaine, Amphetamines, and Other Stimulants

FDA approved in adults:

None

Not FDA approved (used off-label):

Anti-craving and anti-anxiety medications—These medications, such as gabapentin, topiramate, acamprosate, oxcarbazepine, and baclofen, are often helpful.

Bupropion (Wellbutrin)—This is a dopamine-stabilizing medication that is often helpful. Sometimes, it is prescribed in tandem with naltrexone to treat methamphetamine use disorder, resulting in fewer positive drug screens (see below).

Naltrexone (ReVia, Vivitrol)—This opiod blocker also has shown some promise in decreasing cravings and use. A 2021 study by the National Institute on Drug Abuse found that over 12 weeks, patients with methamphetamine use disorder that took bupropion daily and monthly extended-release naltrexone had fewer methamphetamine-positive urine drug screens than those that received a placebo (Trivedi et al., 2021).

L-Methyl Folate or Delta-Folate—These prescribed medical foods are often helpful (Jaeckle, 2014).

When and Why Medications Might Be Used in Treatment

There are different stages of treatment and various reasons that doctors may prescribe medication for addiction treatment:

- Detoxification/withdrawal
- Early recovery
- Maintenance/recovery
- Relapse prevention

Detoxification and Withdrawal

We prescribe medications to help people going through drug or alcohol detox, as the symptoms of detox and withdrawal are truly horrible and, in some rare cases, life-threatening.

When someone has been chronically using a drug of addiction, significant neuroadaptation occurs, and when the drug use stops, the brain cells and receptors have to readapt.

Neurotransmitters affect the brain and other parts of the body. The body also goes through physical symptoms of withdrawal. For opioid withdrawal, body and brain symptoms include sweating, shaking, nausea, diarrhea, running

Neuroadaptation: A process whereby the brain cells and brain chemistry adjust to compensate for a brain-altering substance being present. The acute result is the brain functioning normally, but the longer-term result is substance tolerance, dependence, and when without it, withdrawal.

Dope sickness: Experiencing negative feelings—both physical and mental—of withdrawal of an opioid, such as heroin, pain pills, methadone, buprenorphine, morphine, or hydromorphone. Symptoms may include nausea, vomiting, headache, restlessness, anxiety, hot flashes and cold chills, bone and joint aches, stomach cramping, muscle cramping, restless legs, insomnia, and diarrhea. Symptoms usually last three to four days, but can last longer if the opioid is a longer-acting drug such as methadone. Dope sickness is not life threatening, but people who have gone through it say they felt like they were dying.

nose, chills and hot flashes, muscle twitches/restless legs, agitation, anxiety, sleep difficulties, and more. This is what people call being dope sick. Many patients who have been taking opioid medication as prescribed by doctors may not be aware that they are experiencing withdrawal or dope sickness. They may think they are going through a horrible flu or new-onset disease and may seek medical assistance.

Dope sickness can last three to four days for most, but for some people, depending on certain biological factors, the type of opioid drug, and the drug's half-life, the symptoms can last for several weeks.

Those suffering from opioid withdrawal will say that it feels like they are dying, and sometimes they threaten or attempt suicide during this time. However, opioid withdrawal is usually not life-threatening. With that being said, management of the withdrawal symptoms with medication can help a user move more easily into recovery and sobriety.

Medication types used for opioid detoxification/withdrawal are:
- Opioid-based agonist (methadone, buprenorphine)
- Non-opioid based supportive medications to help with physical and mental symptoms (lofexidine)
- Antagonist based (naltrexone)

Alcohol, benzodiazepines (such as Ativan, Xanax, Valium and more), and barbiturates (such as phenobarbital) work in the gamma aminobutyric acid (GABA) system of the brain. Neuroadaptation in that system causes an imbalance of the inhibitory/excitatory system. If someone with chronic use stops these substances, they may have issues with the brain and body becoming too physiologically excited. These symptoms include increased anxiety, increased heart rate, increased blood pressure, heart palpitations, tremor, agitation, confusion, and even a seizure. Alcohol, benzodiazepine, and barbiturate withdrawal symptoms that are risky and life-threatening are severe confusion and seizures. Withdrawal from these substances should always be medically managed.

Medication treatment types for alcohol, benzodiazepine, and barbiturate withdrawal include tapering doses of benzodiazepines or barbiturates with or without the addition of anti-epileptic medication. The sleep cycle is highly disturbed during withdrawal, so it is beneficial to have a sleep aid in conjunction with the treatment.

Withdrawal from other drugs, such as cocaine, amphetamines, marijuana, or designer drugs, is uncomfortable physically and mentally, yet there are no prescribed protocols to treat the withdrawal medically. It is best to treat the wide variety of symptoms of withdrawal from each of these substances individually.

Non-typical treatments that are effective for drug/alcohol detoxification/withdrawal:

Percutaneous neurostimulator (Bridge, ST Genesis)—An electrical impulse device that is applied to the ear and worn for several days. It stimulates the cranial nerves around the ear, which reduces neuron (fight-or-flight) activity and reduces opioid withdrawal symptoms. Sometimes, these are used for chronic pain, working in the same areas that they work for detox.

Acupuncture— Your acupuncturist will be able to treat you on a daily basis to help repair neuroadaptation and treat withdrawal symptoms (Bemis, Ryan, 2013). During detox, some patients respond best to daily sessions.

Amino acid combination therapy—There are oral and intravenous amino acid formulas that are specially balanced to help the body detox from opioids and help the brain recalibrate (Blum, 2016).

Glutathione: Glutathione is found in every cell, essentially protecting the mitochondria (the powerhouses of the cells) from damage. Glutathione is a long-acting antioxidant that we make naturally from amino acids that we get from the foods we eat. Stress, medications, and drugs deplete our supply of glutathione, thus increasing the possibility of cellular damage.

N-Acetylcysteine (NAC)—An amino acid and precursor to glutathione (see "Glutathione" above), NAC is safe and effective as part of treatment for withdrawal from all drugs, but has been primarily studied in cocaine and opioid withdrawal (Echevarria et al., 2017; McClure et al., 2014).

Nicotinamide adenine dinucleotide (NAD+)—NAD+ (oral, intramuscular, patch, IV, other routes) has been shown to increase glutathione, as well as many other benefits of cellular health and oxidative damage repair (Braidy et al., 2020).

Early Recovery and Maintenance

In early recovery, medications can be necessary to promote the ability to be attentive, process therapeutic interventions, change patterns, and make life and lifestyle changes. The brain's reward system has been hijacked, and many people may need a crutch for a while. Treating the symptoms that one is experiencing is a good tactic. Many patients do not describe any one disorder, (like major depression, generalized anxiety, attention deficit), but suffer from many treatable symptoms from many disorders. The symptoms tend to be the opposite of what the substance, or most effective reward, was.

One way to approach treatment during early recovery (and sometimes maintenance) is to treat the patient using a medication that works in the same location in the brain's reward system that the abused substance was affecting. There are multiple possibilities in treating opioid abuse—an agonist, a partial agonist, or an antagonist. An agonist, such as a full opioid like methadone, turns on the receptors full-time. Buprenorphine, a partial agonist, partially turns on and partially turns off the receptors simultaneously, creating a ceiling effect that provides only a limited reward. And an antagonist blocks the opioid receptors entirely. The opioid blockers on the market are: short-acting naloxone (Narcan) for the rescue of an opioid overdose, medium-acting daily pill form of naltrexone (ReVia), or long-acting monthly injection form of naltrexone (Vivitrol).

There are specific benefits from each of these medications. A knowledgeable addiction doctor will be able to help patients choose from the medications and treatments best suited to their recoveries, taking each patient's unique set of symptoms into account.

Cravings and Relapse Prevention

In any recovery stage, it is crucial to have tools to prevent relapse and to treat cravings. Therapy and cognitive tools are beneficial, but medications can help, too. The medications are similar to those prescribed in early recovery and maintenance (see page 45), but there are fewer that are specific for cravings and relapse prevention.

Anti-craving medications include acamprosate for alcohol, varenicline for nicotine, and buprenorphine or naltrexone for opioids. Naltrexone has been shown to have anti-craving effects for alcohol as well. As more research is completed, naltrexone will likely have indications for craving reduction for any addiction, including gambling or sex addiction, because naltrexone modulates the relationship to the brain's enkephalins (natural opioids) with the resulting dopamine spike (Aboujaoude & Salame, 2016), as was the case with the study of naltrexone to treat methamphetamine addiction (see page 41), and the development of the medication Contrave, naltrexone with bupropion as a weight-loss medication to control food cravings.

Relapse prevention, although it seems it would be identical to anti-craving, is distinct from it. As addiction is a chronic, relapsing disease of the brain's reward system, it is understood that relapse may occur. Sometimes relapse is premeditated, even subconsciously so. For example, someone may wake up and decide to skip a therapy appointment and then start isolating, skipping peer events, and then, even days or weeks later, seek the drug and use it.

Suppose all the tools are in place, such as craving medications, mood medications, psychosocial support, and more. In that case, he may be able to abort the potential relapse before getting the drug.

The other type of relapse is a subconscious impulsive relapse, which is like being on autopilot. If you have ever been driving and become distracted by stressful thoughts or an intense conversation and ended up somewhere well-known to you other than your destination, you well understand autopilot. When a patient relapses, he often says it was like being on autopilot, without conscious thought.

A young man three months sober from heroin told me that he went for a walk to cool off after a stressful day at work and a difficult conversation with his wife. On the walk, he ran into someone he used to use with, and the next thing he knew, he had injected heroin. He barely remembered the events' sequence, similar to being on autopilot while driving and ending up at the wrong location. A relapse like this could easily lead right back to chronic use. Medication can thwart this by changing the brain chemistry and, in the case of an opioid blocker, extinguish the relapse's reward. This makes the relapse non-pleasurable, thereby causing a negative reinforcing experience.

Recovery Maintenance

The maintenance phase of treatment is any time after acute recovery, months to decades after addiction treatment. The goal of maintenance is long-term wellness and stability, which includes health-forward thinking and a balanced lifestyle.

Medications may be helpful for the long term if they are promoting health and wellness. Many of the treatments in this phase are similar to those in the early stages of recovery. These medications reduce or eliminate cravings; block the effects of illicit opioids, so if one does slip up, the addiction cycle does not set back in; restore normal physiology; and promote psychosocial rehabilitation and a nondrug lifestyle.

There is a phenomenon of post-acute withdrawal, or extended symptoms of withdrawal, beyond physiological norms. Usually, the patient has some psychological needs not met and experiences uncomfortable ongoing symptoms because of biological deficiencies. Symptoms can include sleeplessness, cravings, leg cramps, nightmares, anxiety, muscle and joint pain, hyperalgesia (increased pain), and more. In post-acute withdrawal cases, we treat the symptoms with more preventive medications, improved nutrition including supplementation to "build the foundation" (see chapter 5), lifestyle changes, and psychotherapy.

Harm Reduction

Harm reduction is a philosophy and set of principles using strategies to minimize individual and public health risks associated with substance use. It may involve medication and medical intervention. Harm reduction incorporates safer use and can include needle exchange programs, mitigating the risk of

Harm-Reduction Principles

- Working to minimize harmful effects.
- Accepting that substance use exists.
- Understanding that substance use is complex and that some ways of using are less harmful than others.
- Striving for quality of individual and community health, not necessarily abstinence.
- Providing non-judgmental and non-coercive services.
- Treatment goals developed with patient and provider, focusing on decreasing risky behavior and increasing healthy lifestyle.

transfer of hepatitis or HIV, and sometimes opioid replacement, with medications such as methadone and buprenorphine.

Some treatment facilities and criminal justice settings still frown upon harm reduction as a model. However, evidence shows that incorporating harm-reduction principles into treatment can be effective for public health and individual health, essentially meeting the patient where they are with resources, nonjudgement, and hope (Pan & Wood, 2020).

BUILDING THE FOUNDATION

From the subcellular level to the social level, multiple systems are impaired during ongoing substance use and lifestyle.

The brain requires stable and balanced nutrients to function and a whole system in place to function well. During sustained substance use, most people live lifestyles that reduce or deplete their nutritional stores. Immune systems may become impaired, chronic inflammation may occur, and vitamin and hormone deficiencies become the norm. Recovery maintenance is a perfect time to make health-forward changes to rebuild the foundation by adding nutrition to the cells' building blocks and enhancing neuron repair and growth.

Gut

The gastrointestinal system plays a significant role in brain health and vice-versa (Kirch, 2008). There is a relatively new field of study of the microbiome and the gut-brain axis, helping us understand that our gut bacteria influence cognitive functioning, learning, memory, decision making, mood, and even cravings (Butler et al., 2019).

The gut has the same neurotransmitters and receptors as the brain, but the brain does the executive functioning. The three to five pounds of the thousand-plus types of bacteria in the gut make by-products that influence your chemical makeup, thereby affecting how genes and proteins fold and work. Neurotransmitters are among those proteins. A history of antibiotic use and diet, especially eating processed foodss, can negatively influence the flora makeup.

Basic nutrition awareness helps tremendously to treat an unhealthy gut.

- Add full-spectrum prebiotic foods (non-digestible fiber, usually six grams a day of foods, such as raw chicory root, raw artichoke, raw dandelion greens, leeks, onions, asparagus, wheat bran, bananas, and more; cooked versions of the suggested raw items have a lower amount of prebiotic but are still viable). Add a healthy probiotic (microorganisms) of at least 12 billion cultures per dose and at least eight different bacteria strains. Some bacteria are being formulated to target specific disease states; recent research on certain strains targets depression and anxiety. We are soon likely to find ones that will help with addiction and cravings.

- "Eat real food, not too much, mostly plants," as Michael Pollan famously said in *The Omnivore's Dilemma*. *Real food* means that every ingredient should be something you understand and can pronounce, so no processed foods (Chronicle et al., n.d.).

- Add L-glutamine. This is an abundant amino acid that heals many tissues in the body, especially in the digestive tract. It is calming and is known to help with anxiety as well as sugar and alcohol cravings. Anecdotal evidence suggests that it helps with drug cravings as well.

Gut Bacteria

The human microbiome consists of trillions of bacteria that are working within a person's body. Most of the bacteria are in the gut, but some are on the skin and elsewhere. Our native bacteria (microbiome) interface with our biology to influence health, behavior, and general functioning. Research indicates that there is a highly synergistic relationship between these gut bacteria, human health, and even epigenetics.

The Omnivore's Dilemma: A nonfiction book written by Michael Pollan and published in 2006. The book studies the ecology of food and eating, questioning the status quo and inspiring discourse on the question, "What is food?"

Neurogenesis

We used to think that once you stunted or killed a brain cell, it was gone forever, but we now know that this is false! We now know about neurogenesis (growing of new neurons) and synaptogenesis (making new synapses, the cellular communication pathways between neurons), both of which can occur under favorable conditions. Studies show that dietary nutrients can increase neurogenesis and synaptogenesis in mammals (Parker, 2016; Poulose et al., 2017).

- Antioxidants are chemicals that prevent damage from free radicals; they include flavonoids (in cacao, blueberries, açai berries, and more), vitamin E, green tea (or extract), and curcumin (found in turmeric).
- Omega-3 fatty acids, flaxseed, and fish (particularly wild-caught, coldwater fish), which are known to decrease cognitive decline and help stimulate brain health.
- Supplements, especially zinc and vitamin A, may stimulate the birth of new cells.

Hormones

Many drugs can alter hormone levels by inhibiting the brain's ability to make them. Often, chronic opioid use downregulates the cascade that makes testosterone. It is prudent to test the blood levels of vitamin D, testosterone, and dehydroepiandrosterone (DHEA), and treat them if they are low. There are hormone specialists, as well as nutritionists and other providers, who are well equipped to help people augment and repair hormone levels.

Nutritional Supplementation for Methylation

Methylation is one of the most common chemical reactions in the body. It plays an essential role in detoxification, neurotransmitter synthesis, protein synthesis, DNA protection, folate metabolism, cardiovascular health, hormone regulation, inflammation reduction, and more. We need foods and supplements to make sure that we have enough methyl groups to methylate the

Methylation: This is one of the most fundamental biochemical processes in every cell of your brain and body, crucial to a range of bodily functions. Specifically, methylation is the donation of a methyl group (carbon plus two hydrogen molecules) to an amino acid. Amino acids are the building blocks of proteins. The body cannot function without proteins.

Methylation of certain amino acids is crucial for:
Maintaining DNA energy
Increased immune function
Decreasing inflammation
Detoxification
Mood enhancement

Poor methylation may contribute to many conditions, including:
Heart disease
Adult neurological conditions
Chronic fatigue
Autism spectrum
Miscarriages and implantation and pregnancy problems
Allergies and other immune-system issues
Digestive problems
Aging and age-related disease
Diabetes

required pathways. Substance use depletes the reserve, as does eating processed foods and not having a balanced healthy diet.

So, stay away from processed foods, eat quinoa, leafy greens, and beets, and for meats, stick to organic chicken, lamb and fish.

Increase Glutathione

Glutathione is a powerful antioxidant that protects cells from damage, and, in the brain, it plays a key role in the dopamine reward system (Kreutzer et al., 2011). Long-term drug use interferes with normal glutathione regulation in the brain (Womersley & Uys, 2016).

- NAC—N-acetylcysteine, usually found in the form of a supplement, has been shown to increase glutathione concentrations in brain tissue and increase dopamine release. Some studies show decreased anxiety and irritability (Sotres-Bayon et al., 2006).
- NAD+—Nicotinamide adenine dinucleotide (oral, intramuscular, patch, IV, other routes) has been shown to increase glutathione, as well as many other benefits of cellular health and oxidative damage repair (Braidy et al., 2020).

Biological Wellness Regimen

- Take B-complex, zinc, NAC, and magnesium
- Take trimethylglycine (Betaine)
- Gut health: Probiotic
- Check your MTHFR gene—if you have a genetic mutation, supplement with an active form of folate, such as L-Methyl Folate or Delta-Folate (in the form of the prescribed vitamins Deplin or Enlyte)
- Minimize sugar intake
- Anti-inflammatory supplements: Omega-3 (High EPA/ DHA) and Curcumin

- Physical activity—Healthy and balanced fitness activities that suit your body are ideal. A minimum of 150 minutes of low-impact cardio per week is shown to increase antioxidants and improve inflammation recovery. Consistency is key.

Healthy Relationships

The prefrontal cortex has better stability when relationships are healthy. Chaotic, punishing, and negative relationships downregulate the brain's ability to produce and use ample serotonin and dopamine that lower mood and increase relapse risk (see chapter 8).

Therapy

The brain is an organ, and although it is not exactly a muscle, it can act like one. It can get stronger with working out. Brain pathways are strengthened with repetition. Therapy identifies patterns of thinking that have strong pathways set up and attempts to reframe those patterns. Synapse patterns, or patterns of thinking, can be negative or positive, unhealthy or healthy. Therapy helps move away from harmful, unhealthy patterns of thinking by strengthening the "muscle" with healthy patterns.

Sleep

Many addiction treatment philosophies suggest that sleep problems are just something to wait out until sleep normalizes. Sound sleep is essential for brain healing, synapse recovery, and resilience, so I treat sleep disturbances as an acute problem. Anyone with sleep issues, with or without addiction, feels psychologically unhealthy and has a more challenging time healing.

Some over-the-counter sleep aids with good recovery effects include valerian root, melatonin, lavender, chamomile, 5-HTP, L-theanine, L-tryptophan, and magnesium. Many people take antihistamines for sleep, such as Benadryl, Unisom, or Tylenol PM. Although they are effective for sleep, they disrupt the sleep cycle and decrease restorative sleep, so they are not preferred.

There are many nonaddictive prescribed sleep aids, most off-label for sleep. The best ones for brain healing do not disrupt sleep cycle stages.

Sleep devices are also very useful, such as FDA authorized electrotherapy devices, for example, the Alpha-Stim. There are also digital therapeutics (apps) for insomnia, some by prescription, such as Somryst.

Exercise

The body is all around more resilient with regular exercise. The brain responds well to exercise, naturally enhancing hedonic tone (see page 19) with increased dopamine, serotonin, and endorphins. At a minimum of 150 minutes a week, regular cardiovascular exercise can help the heart respond better to anxiety. Exercise can include meditation as well, which is also proven healthy for the brain, anxiety, and cravings. There are many anecdotes of people with addiction finding a type of yoga or martial art that suits them, changing their brain chemistry so much that they never have a craving or a relapse again.

IV NAD+ Therapy

An emerging type of treatment for addiction and overall brain health, this intravenous nicotinamide adenine dinucleotide (IV NAD+) therapy (Braidy et al., 2020) is a natural coenzyme that has a significant role in maintaining the energy of all the cells in the body by working in ATP-producing pathways in the mitochondria (powerhouses of the cells). NAD+ deficiency is common when a person has many stressors and has been using drugs and alcohol and also maintaining poor nutrition. NAD+ deficiency usually manifests as fatigue, low mood, anxiety, and other physical illnesses. By using IV NAD+ therapy, the cells have quick access to powering up, restructuring, and repairing structures, especially in the brain.

IV NAD+ is usually offered in an outpatient setting. Patients receive daily

IV therapy, taking many hours a day for some. The suggested time frame is a 10-day regimen for detox from opioids and alcohol, in particular. Patients tell me that the treatment helped kick-start their cognition and brain health, feeling like the fog was gone—like they had been sober six months already instead of just over a week.

As with all treatments for addiction, NAD+ therapy is a tool in the toolbox and may have greater effect if used in conjunction with other therapies.

Summary: A Basic Regimen

Although the regimen presented below does not encompass every aspect of all of the recommendations, this is a formula I recommend to many people during early recovery. It is not individualized, and some patients may not require all of these . . . or they may require more. All supplements can be purchased at a health-food or supplement store. The best supplements are those that are third-party tested.

Note: Always work with your physician or nutritionist when starting new supplements. Some may be contraindicated or conflict with medications you take, and some may have toxic side-effects if taken at doses too high for you. Ideally, meet with a functional medicine specialist or a nutritionist specializing in cognitive optimization and/or addiction for exact dose recommendations and additional suggestions.

Physiological Wellness Regimen

- Healthy relationships
- Meditation/mindfulness
- Individual therapy
- Peer supports: 12-step, fellowship, Al-Anon, Dharma Recovery, SMART recovery, Life Ring, and others
- Exercise
- Sleep

PAIN AND ADDICTION

Many people with addiction have chronic pain. Often, pain management for true pain was part of their path to addiction (along with biology and genetics) in the first place. Treating pain is difficult for everyone, but even more so for someone with addiction, either active or in recovery.

People with addiction often have hypersensitive pain receptors that may make it even more difficult. However, there are many excellent tools to use. Noncancer pain can truly be effectively treated without chronic opioid use most of the time. However, short-term opioid pain management is sometimes necessary, particularly after an accident or during and after surgery.

Acute pain management with opioids is medically useful, but it should be limited to three to six months while starting other treatments to manage the pain's root cause.

Some effective treatments:

- Non-opioid medications, such as non-steroidal anti-inflammatory drugs (NSAIDS, such as ibuprofen), gabapentin, duloxetine, and pregabalin, can all be effective for modulating pain, decreasing inflammation, and decreasing anxiety related to pain.
- Physical therapy is excellent to maximize strength, range of motion, and flexibility and to rehabilitate the musculoskeletal system to be in the best shape.

- Acupuncture is widely accepted for pain treatment, both chronic and acute (Hempel et al., 2014).
- "Pacing activities" involve learning to do physical work up to a point and stopping before the pain starts.
- Massage therapy is very effective for decreasing pain. Massage therapy improves circulation, decreases inflammation, increases range of motion, and helps muscles and ligaments get "unstuck." Also, massage increases serotonin, which lowers anxiety, improves mood, and increases deep sleep, which naturally reduces pain.
- Electrical stimulation, such as TENS units or e-stim, are excellent in pain management. This process delivers very low electrical currents through electrodes placed on the skin. The electrical impulses disrupt the pain message sent from the nerves to the brain and also stimulate the production of the body's own pain relievers (DeSantana et al., 2008).

There may be a time that an addict needs to take opioid pain medicine for surgery or acute pain. The best outcomes involve an informed doctor and supportive family. Patients must discuss honestly with their doctors their addiction histories and their concerns. The patient, family, and physician can then make a plan as to how and by whom the medications are given, as well as a safety plan. Often, the patient in recovery will request that a family member hold and dispense his or her medications. And the physician can assist by monitoring closely with pill counts, more frequent and smaller prescriptions, and a plan to taper off the opioid pain pill.

Frequently, patients tell me that their surgeons or other pain pill prescribers will give them a large quantity of pain pills with no restriction, followed by refills upon refills, and then, at some point, will cut them off. Physical tolerance has now been built up, and, often, the pain has not been managed preventively, so the pain is worse. Meanwhile, the patient is suffering from opioid withdrawal to boot. The way to prevent this is for the treating physician to have a plan to taper, then safely stop, pain medication.

PREGNANCY AND ADDICTION

All drug abuse is harmful in pregnancy. There is no difference between a pregnant woman suffering from addiction and a nonpregnant person suffering from addiction, except that there is the pregnancy and fetus to consider. A pregnant woman using heroin is a heroin abuser who just happens to be pregnant.

Some physicians shy away from asking pregnant women about addiction and substance use. The 2015 American College of Obstetricians and Gynecologists (ACOG) guidelines include asking specific questions about substances (The American College of Obstetricians and Gynecologists, 2015). This can be scary for some soon-to-be mothers, as some states still consider addicted mothers to be criminals and may enforce legal consequences.

There is no reason not to treat a pregnant woman for addiction. It can help the mother, the child, and the whole family tremendously. Some medication choices are different for pregnant women because of potential harm to the fetus. For example, when treating alcohol addiction, naltrexone and carbamazepine are great medications, but they may cause harm to the fetus, so doctors will stay away from them.

Regarding opioid addiction, the gold standard used to be to transition a pregnant woman from opioids (heroin, pain pills) to methadone. There have been numerous studies over the past decade showing that buprenorphine has equal outcomes for pregnant women with opioid addiction and that the newborn babies do much better. A problem of a newborn being exposed to opioids in utero is neonatal opioid withdrawal syndrome (NOWS). A 2014 meta-analysis (a study that reviews other studies) reported that babies born to buprenorphine-treated mothers had an average of 7.23 fewer days in the hospital after birth than those born to methadone-treated mothers, with less NOWS and less need for medication to treat the withdrawal (Jones et al., 2012). The buprenorphine-born babies had better weight, length, and head circumference and also were born closer to term than the methadone-born babies.

Some treatment facilities will take women who are pregnant, and some actually specialize in this population. If you or someone you know is pregnant and struggling with opioid addiction, be sure to talk with the admissions at a treatment facility to ensure that they are willing and able to treat addiction during pregnancy. Also, some obstetricians may be uncomfortable working with someone using or trying to stop using. I have known obstetricians who fire patients for having a positive drug screen. In questioning these doctors, I have been told, "These stupid women choose drugs over motherhood." Not all obstetricians understand that addiction is a disease, and patients—pregnant or not—need to be treated accordingly. Be sure to discuss with your obstetrician, and if merited and possible, find an obstetrician that will work with your needs.

Neonatal abstinence syndrome (NAS): A group of symptoms that the newborn experiences because of exposure to opioids while in the womb. The symptoms are the same as adult opioid withdrawal symptoms but have more complications because the newborn is more susceptible and more fragile than an adult. Treatment includes admission to the neonatal intensive care unit (NICU), full monitoring, and administering of medications to prevent severe withdrawal symptoms.

LOVED ONES' ROLES AND EXPECTATIONS

It is difficult to see a loved one suffer with addiction and its complications. It is hard on the whole family. The family reacts and starts setting up patterns of behavior to respond to the addiction and things that go along with it. This is why addiction is often called a family disease.

Remember, the brain is incredibly complex to treat, because doing the thing that is healthy for this organ is controlled by the organ itself. Again, think of someone with two injured hands and the only way to heal the hands is to salve and wrap them, but they are too injured to do so.

Addiction is a family problem but not necessarily a family disease (yet it often has genetic and biological underpinnings). Nonetheless, the whole family gets to participate in change. There is an 85 percent improved success rate for addiction when families and loved ones get involved, are supportive, and learn new patterns of behavior (Cleveland et al., 2005).

I have seen many patients whose loved ones expect to drop off the patient at a facility for a few weeks or months and then pick them up "fixed," with everything "normal." No matter how perfect the treatment program and how great the patient does while there, very rarely do patients come home to the same patterns and environment and find it easy to stay in recovery.

I like to think of a plank barge with a family standing on top in the center. If someone starts suffering from addiction, he or she tips the balance—that person goes over to one corner. To maintain balance, the other family members have to run to other edges. Once the person with addiction gets help and starts changing patterns and behaviors, he or she comes back to the center. Now the barge is tipping because the rest of the family has to move. This is representative of how the dynamic must change for everyone to be healthy.

A loved one should understand that addiction is a disease and the behaviors that come with it are outcroppings of this disease. Sometimes this alone can help loved ones feel less like blaming, shaming, and punishing the person with addiction. As most people can imagine, receiving blame and shame feels horrible. The brain of one receiving blame and shame actually will modify the amount of usable dopamine and serotonin, thereby making one feel worse (Podesta & Hussey, 2019). With lower dopamine tone, there is a higher likelihood to seek a drug and relapse.

The ideal role of a loved one is a good balance of support and love without blaming and shaming and with good boundaries to prevent enabling (see page 12). This is very complicated and difficult to achieve, but with practice and support, it is possible. Al-Anon has great support for family members or loved ones of those with addiction. I always recommend that loved ones familiarize themselves with this group and attend at least a handful of meetings.

The person with addiction may or may not be seeking recovery. If he or she needs help but is not interested, the first step for the family is being sure to not enable it. I know a father who is perplexed that his adult son keeps relapsing on pain pills, and then the father is distraught when the son leaves for weeks at a time. But, every time the son comes back, he is broke. The father rescues his son by giving him money. When the son was arrested for selling drugs, the father rescued him by bailing him out of jail and hiring an expensive lawyer who was able to get the charge expunged.

The son knows he can rely on his father to rescue him. The father believes he is helping his son. He is equating money and legal help with love and support, yet he is, in fact, enabling his son's addiction.

I saw a patient in his fifties who was the end result of this sort of enabling. His father and brother are judges, and they all live in a small town. As early as 16 years old, this patient was charged with his first drunk-driving offense. His father had it expunged, thinking he was protecting his son. Over the next 40 years, the son had more than 15 DWIs, damaged a significant amount of property, and even was charged with involuntary manslaughter. Every single charge was dropped, and he was never required to take responsibility or make any changes to his patterns. He was seeing me because an employer finally required that he get treatment in order to keep his job. His family was not able to rescue him from this consequence. Now, he is starting the process of recovery, facing all the regrets and fears that he has suppressed, and unlearning the expectation that he is without responsibility for his actions.

Help Prevent Enabling

- Set up honest two-way communication, without imparting shame and emotional punishment.
- Set up clear and consistent boundaries.
- Give loving help and support when the addict is on track.
- Give guidance and recommendations when the addict wants help getting on track.
- Pull back when relapse occurs; seek support for yourself during that time.
- Relinquish control of things that are beyond your control. Remember the "Serenity Prayer:"

The Serenity Prayer is a prayer written by the American theologian Reinhold Niebuhr[1][2] (1892–1971). It is commonly quoted as:

God, grant me the serenity to accept the things I cannot change, courage to change the things I can, and wisdom to know the difference.

Relapse—What Does the Family Do?

Addiction is a chronic relapsing disease of the brain. Just as a diabetic in good treatment might have an anomalous blood sugar increase, and just as a cancer in remission might come back, an addict might relapse.

When relapse occurs, get good support for yourself while making recommendations to the person with addiction. Although we would love to be able to control it, we cannot. We can only control our own situations. We can help the person struggling with addiction by changing the dynamic and offering support.

On average, a person with addiction will relapse 13 times. As time passes, usually each relapse will be worse. But every recovery is better.

Help Prevent Relapse

- Removal or lessening of trauma and drama
- Enhanced coping skills, both of individual and family
- Loving and honest relationships
- Feelings of mental wellness
- Physical and mental activity
- Supportive medications, when necessary, for cravings, mental health, and physical health

Trust

Often, when a patient returns home after treatment, the hardest part is building or rebuilding trust. After so much hurt has occurred and relationships are damaged, it is natural to be untrusting. Both parties, patient and family, must be aware that trust has to be earned. The patient returning home, especially after several months of recovery and treatment, may feel that he or she deserves to be trusted immediately, since he or she has done so much work. But,

A Plan for Early Recovery

- Make sure to have a system in place, with phone numbers and support available to the person in early recovery.
- Let go, and let the system do its job.
- Work on yourself, as only a stable self and family can be supportive to others.
- Get educated about addiction. (Like reading this book!)
- When family and patients are ready, do family sessions with a mediator or therapist, and involve the family in the treatment plan with the patient's treatment provider.
- Avoid micromanaging the patient, because this breeds the old dynamic. Change the family dynamic.

that work was not with the family, so the family must respond with giving trust when merited and be aware not to fall back into the fears of what happened before treatment. Trust will be established incrementally, not all at once. This helps both parties—the patient feels responsibility and accountability, and the family feels some regulation in the household.

The patient and family do the best when the patient does not hide the struggles with addiction. This disease is prevalent. Shame and guilt lower healthy neurotransmitters, increasing risk of relapse. Hiding the struggles causes shame and guilt, undermining the recovery.

Acknowledge that the primary and most significant thing for the person with addiction is getting into and being in recovery. Do not assume that they are fixed once abstinent and that they can get back to normal life. Avoid putting pressures on the person with addiction to immediately fix legal situations, settle finances, get a job, and so on.

EXPERIMENTATION VERSUS ADDICTION

Not everyone that tries a drug will get hooked and become addicted.

Risk of Abuse / Addiction

Although most illicit drug use starts in the teen years and up to 40 percent of 10th graders say that they have tried drugs, addiction affects about 10 percent of the population (Lipari & Park-Lee, 2019). The earlier someone tries a drug, the more it affects the biology, and the more likely he or she is to become addicted. Someone is 50 percent more likely to become an addict if he or she starts using substances regularly before age 18 (Odgers et al., 2008).

I have seen many adult patients with psychiatric needs, not addiction, who give a story about getting caught experimenting with drugs in high school and being taken to a rehabilitation or boot camp. Many report that they have deep resentments toward their families once they return home and have lifelong family strife because of these resentments. This is a concern when deciding as to whether rehabilitation is the answer.

An editor shared the following: "When my son went to his first boot camp/rehab, he went in an amateur and came out an expert on how to use, where to get, how to improvise administering the drug, and, of course, with a full list of contacts for scoring drugs. It was really a bad turning point for him."

We do not know if experimentation by a teen will lead to addiction. However, we know that exposure to substances can affect the developing brain and potentially increase addiction risk. (Nestler EJ: Epigenetic mechanisms of drug addiction. *Neuropharmacology* 2014;76 Pt B:259–268) The best strategy is preventing experimentation by fostering an honest, safe, and loving environment, with education on the risks of trying certain things.

During stressful transitions, such as moving, changing schools, and any parental difficulties, the teen is more likely to try a drug. If a teen in the house is starting to experiment, some sort of response is needed, but it will not necessarily involve rehab.

There are pacts with school, organized sports, and youth organizations that commit to no drug use and regular drug testing. Sometimes, these programs use contingency planning, i.e. giving a reward.

First, the family should create an open discussion with the teen to understand the extent and intent of use. It can be beneficial to involve one of his or her respected peers. There are a handful of organizations and tools that can help. A reward-based system is very effective, as teens are constantly seeking rewards.

If difficulties still occur and substance use escalates, the family may seek a therapeutic evaluation to help with guidance. Just as for adults, there are all levels of care and treatment. It is even more essential for a teen that the family be very involved and the family dynamic shifts. And, just as in adults, substance use may be a manifestation of a stressor and may not be the root cause. It is paramount to address stressors and coping skills.

Rehabilitation might not be the right tool. Many teens are brought to rehabilitation to learn recovery and abstinence when what they really need is for the stressors to be addressed. If the wrong tool is used, it will not work.

INTERVENTIONS

For all ages, when addiction is rampant and the individual is unwilling or unable to get help, consider an intervention. An intervention usually includes initial sessions with the family only, not the person with the addiction. During this time, an interventionist will assess the need, provide thorough education to the family about addiction and treatment types, and then train and rehearse for the intervention.

Then, either at home or in the office, the intervention will occur at a planned time. It is usually a surprise to the person with the addiction, although most of my patients who have gone through an intervention will say they had an idea that it was coming. During the intervention, the therapist and family will use therapeutic skills, including motivational enhancement, to help get individuals with addiction to agree to treatment.

The interventionist will then make a facilitated referral to an appropriate fit for the patient's needs. Usually, the interventionist will also support making travel arrangements and help handle logistics and coordination of getting the patient into treatment. Often the interventionist will also follow up once the patient is in treatment.

An addiction interventionist must be a professional with an expertise in addiction, who also has a vast knowledge of treatment facilities of all different levels of care, cost, and structure. Often he or she is an LCSW (licensed clinical social worker), LPC (licensed professional counselor), or psychologist (PhD or PsyD). Sometimes, an addiction doctor may be involved. An interventionist should not be a marketer for, or an employee of, a particular rehab facility. There is a professional certification for an interventionist, and few professionals have gotten the certification.

CONCLUSION

Risk of Abuse / Addiction

Comprehensive treatment requires treating any and all pertinent parts of addiction.

Addiction is a complex and difficult problem that affects not just the individual but the surrounding family and friends. Throughout this book, I have covered approaches to treatment of the biology, the stressors, and the drug use. With the tools in this book, you and a treatment professional can develop a comprehensive treatment plan for your or your loved one's needs. If you or a family member with substance issues is looking to make a change and you do not already have a treatment provider, check out "Find an Addiction Professional" on page 80.

Some tangible solutions to take away from reading this book:

- Destigmatize addiction.
- Prevent addiction.
- Treat addiction early.
- Treat addiction with as many tools as possible.
- Treat addiction at the right level of care.
- Keep vigilant.

REFERENCES

Aboujaoude, E., & Salame, W. O. (2016). Naltrexone: A pan-addiction treatment? CNS Drugs, 30(8), 719–733. https://doi.org/10.1007/s40263-016-0373-0

Ahmad, F., Rossen, L., & Sutton, P. (2020, December 16). Products—vital statistics rapid release—provisional drug overdose data. CDC. https://cdc.gov/nchs/nvss/vsrr/drug-overdose-data.htm

Alegría-Torres, J., Baccarelli, A., & Bollati, V. (2011). Epigenetics and lifestyle. Epigenomics, 3(3), 267–277. https://doi.org/10.2217/epi.11.22

Alphasigma. (2019). How Deplin works. https://deplin.com/hcp/how-deplin-works

American Psychiatric Association. (2013). Diagnostic and statistical manual of mental disorders v (5th ed.). American Psychiatric Association. https://doi.org/10.1176/appi.books.9780890425596

American Society of Addiction Medicine. (2016, October 8). Use of Naloxone for the prevention of opioid overdose deaths. https://asam.org/advocacy/find-a-policy-statement/view-policy-statement/public-policy-statements/2014/08/28/use-of-naloxone-for-the-prevention-of-drug-overdose-deaths

American Society of Addiction Medicine. (2019, September 15). ASAM definition of addiction. https://asam.org/quality-practice/definition-of-addiction

Bemis, R. (2013). Evidence for the NADA protocol: Summary of research. National Acupuncture Detoxification Assocation. https://acudetox.com/evidence-for-the-nada-protocol-summary-of-research/

Blum, K. (2016). Hypothesizing that a pro-dopaminergic regulator (KB220zTM Liquid Variant) can induce "Dopamine Homeostasis" and provide adjunctive detoxification benefits in opiate/opioid dependence. Clinical Medical Reviews and Case Reports, 3(8). https://doi.org/10.23937/2378-3656/1410125

Braidy, N., Villalva, M. D., & van Eeden, S. (2020). Sobriety and satiety: Is NAD+ the answer? Antioxidants, 9(425). https://doi.org/10.3390/antiox9050425

Butler, M. I., Mörkl, S., Sandhu, K.V., Cryan, J. F., & Dinan, T. G. (2019). The gut microbiome and mental health: What should we tell our patients? Le microbiote intestinal et la santé mentale: Que devrions-nous dire à nos patients? Canadian Journal of Psychiatry. Revue Canadienne De Psychiatrie, 64(11), 747–760. https://doi.org/10.1177/0706743719874168

Cachia, C. (2020, January 16). Psychotherapy may fix serotonin receptors better than anti-depressant drugs. MyCME. https://cme30.eu/psychotherapy-may-fix-serotonin-receptors-better-than-antidepressant-drugs/

Centers for Disease Control and Prevention, National Center for Injury Prevention and Control. (2020, December 7). U.S. opioid dispensing rate maps | drug overdose | CDC injury center. https://cdc.gov/drugoverdose/maps/rxrate-maps.html

Chronicle, H. C. (2010, January 23). How to eat. https://michaelpollan.com/reviews/how-to-eat/

Cleveland, M. J., Gibbons, F. X., Gerrard, M., Pomery, E. A., & Brody, G. H. (2005). The impact of parenting on risk cognitions and risk behavior: A study of mediation and moderation in a panel of African American adolescents. Child Development, 76(4), 900–916. https://doi.org/10.1111/j.1467-8624.2005.00885.x

Crew, B. (2015, February 27). Bennett's wallabies get high on poppy seeds. Australian Geographic. https://australiangeographic.com.au/blogs/creatura-blog/2015/02/bennetts-wallabies-get-high/

DeSantana, J. M., Walsh, D. M., Vance, C., Rakel, B. A., & Sluka, K. A. (2008). Effectiveness of transcutaneous electrical nerve stimulation for treatment of hyperalgesia and pain. Current Rheumatology Reports, 10(6), 492–499.

Dowell, D., Haegerich, T. M., & Chou, R. (2016). CDC guideline for prescribing opioids for chronic pain—United States, 2016. MMWR. Recommendations and Reports, 65(1). https://doi.org/10.15585/mmwr.rr6501e1er

Downey, E., Pan, W., Harrison, J., Poza-Juncal, E., & Tanabe, P. (2017). Implementation of a schedule II patient agreement for opioids and stimulants in an adult primary care practice. Journal of Family Medicine and Primary Care, 6(1), 52–57. https://doi.org/10.4103/2249-4863.214959

Downs, B. W., Blum, K., Baron, D., Bowirrat, A., Lott, L., Brewer, R., Boyett, B., Siwicki, D., Roy, A. K., Podesta, A., Badgaiyan, S., Hajela, R., Fried, L., & Badgaiyan, R. D. (2019). Death by opioids: Are there non-addictive scientific solutions? Journal of Systems and Integrative Neuroscience, 5. https://doi.org/10.15761/JSIN.1000211

Dreher, J.-C., Kohn, P., Kolachana, B., Weinberger, D. R., & Berman, K. F. (2009).

Variation in dopamine genes influences responsivity of the human reward system. Proceedings of the National Academy of Sciences, 106(2), 617–622. https://doi.org/10.1073/pnas.0805517106

Echevarria, M., Reis, T., Capatti, G., Soares, V., Silveira, D., & Fidalgo, T. (2017). N-acetylcysteine for treating cocaine addiction – A systematic review. Psychiatry Research, 251. https://doi.org/10.1016/j.psychres.2017.02.024

Fraser, S., Moore, D., & Keane, H. (2014). Models of Addiction. In Habits: Remaking Addiction (pp. 26–59). Palgrave Macmillan UK. https://doi.org/10.1057/9781137316776_2

Garbely, J. (2017, November 17). How did we get into this fix, and how do we get out? Pennsylvania Academy of Family Physicians and the Reading Hospital CME, Pennsylvania.

Health Resources and Services Administration. (2020, July). Opioid Crisis. Official Web Site of the US Health Resources & Services Administration. https://hrsa.gov/opioids

Heitland, I., Oosting, R. S., Baas, J. M. P., Massar, S. A. A., Kenemans, J. L., & Böcker, K. B. E. (2012). Genetic polymorphisms of the dopamine and serotonin systems modulate the neurophysiological response to feedback and risk taking in healthy humans. Cognitive, Affective, & Behavioral Neuroscience, 12(4), 678–691. https://doi.org/10.3758/s13415-012-0108-8

Hempel, S., Taylor, S. L., Solloway, M. R., Miake-Lye, I., Beroes, J. M., Shanman, R., Booth, M. J., Siroka, A. M., & Shekelle, P. G. (2014). Evidence map of acupuncture. Department of Veterans Affairs. https://pubmed.ncbi.nlm.nih.gov/24575449/

Jaeckle, T. (2014). Patient with major depressive disorder responds to L-Methylfolate post-genetic testing. Journal of Depression and Anxiety, 03(03). https://doi.org/10.4172/2167-1044.1000156

Jones, H. E., Fischer, G., Heil, S. H., Kaltenbach, K., Martin, P. R., Coyle, M. G., Selby, P., Stine, S. M., O'Grady, K. E., & Arria, A. M. (2012). Maternal opioid treatment: Human experimental research (MOTHER) – Approach, issues, and lessons learned. Addiction (Abingdon, England), 107(0 1), 28–35. https://doi.org/10.1111/j.1360-0443.2012.04036.x

Kakko, J., Svanborg, K. D., Kreek, M. J., & Heilig, M. (2003). 1-year retention and social function after buprenorphine-assisted relapse prevention treatment for heroin dependence in Sweden: A randomised, placebo-controlled trial. Lancet (London, England), 361(9358), 662–668. https://doi.org/10.1016/S0140-6736(03)12600-1

Kelly, J. F., Humphreys, K., & Ferri, M. (2020). Alcoholics Anonymous and 12-Step Facilitation programs help people to recover from alcohol problems | Cochrane. Cochrane Database of Systematic Reviews, 3. https://doi.org/10.1002/14651858.CD012880.pub2

Kirch, W. (Ed.). (2008). Encyclopedia of public health. Springer Netherlands. https://doi.org/10.1007/978-1-4020-5614-7

Koegelenberg, C. F. N., Noor, F., Bateman, E. D., van Zyl-Smit, R. N., Bruning, A., O'Brien, J. A., Smith, C., Abdool-Gaffar, M. S., Emanuel, S., Esterhuizen, T. M., & Irusen, E. M. (2014). Efficacy of varenicline combined with nicotine replacement therapy vs varenicline alone for smoking cessation: A randomized clinical trial. JAMA, 312(2), 155. https://doi.org/10.1001/jama.2014.7195

Kreutzer, J. S., DeLuca, J., & Caplan, B. (Eds.). (2011). Encyclopedia of clinical neuropsychology. Springer New York. https://doi.org/10.1007/978-0-387-79948-3

Lipari, R. N., & Park-Lee, E. (2019). Key substance use and mental health indicators in the United States: Results from the 2018 national survey on drug use and health. SAMHSA, 82. https://samhsa.gov/data/sites/default/files/cbhsq-reports/NSDUHNationalFindingsReport2018/NSDUHNationalFindingsReport2018.pdf

Little, J. W., Falace, D. A., Miller, C. S., & Rhodus, N. L. (2013). Chapter 30—Drug and alcohol abuse. In J. W. Little, D. A. Falace, C. S. Miller, & N. L. Rhodus (Eds.), Little and Falace's Dental Management of the Medically Compromised Patient (8th ed., pp. 562–574). Mosby. https://doi.org/10.1016/B978-0-323-08028-6.00030-0

Lovinger, D. M. (2012). Neurobiological basis of drug reward and reinforcement. In Addiction medicine: Science and practice (Vols. 1 and 2) (pp. 255–281). Springer Science + Business Media.

McClure, E. A., Gipson, C. D., Malcolm, R. J., Kalivas, P. W., & Gray, K. M. (2014). Potential role of N-Acetylcysteine in the management of substance use disorders. CNS Drugs, 28(2), 95–106. https://doi.org/10.1007/s40263-014-0142-x

Morgan, D., Grant, K. A., Gage, H. D., Mach, R. H., Kaplan, J. R., Prioleau, O.,

Nader, S. H., Buchheimer, N., Ehrenkaufer, R. L., & Nader, M. A. (2002). Social dominance in monkeys: Dopamine D2 receptors and cocaine self-administration. Nature Neuroscience, 5(2), 169–174. https://doi.org/10.1038/nn798

National Institute on Drug Abuse. (2018, January 1). How effective is drug addiction treatment? National Institute on Drug Abuse. https://drugabuse.gov/publications/principles-drug-addiction-treatment-research-based-guide-third-edition/frequently-asked-questions/how-effective-drug-addiction-treatment

National Institute on Drug Abuse. (2019, August). Genetics and epigenetics of addiction drugfacts. https://drugabuse.gov/publications/drugfacts/genetics-epigenetics-addiction

National Institute on Drug Abuse. (2020, April 6). Costs of substance abuse. https://drugabuse.gov/drug-topics/trends-statistics/costs-substance-abuse

National Institute on Drug Abuse. (2021, January 29). Overdose death rates. https://drugabuse.gov/drug-topics/trends-statistics/overdose-death-rates

Nestler, E. J. (2014). Epigenetic mechanisms of drug addiction. Neuropharmacology, 76(0 0). https://doi.org/10.1016/j.neuropharm.2013.04.004

Odgers, C. L., Caspi, A., Nagin, D. S., Piquero, A. R., Slutske, W. S., Milne, B. J., Dickson, N., Poulton, R., & Moffitt, T. E. (2008). Is it important to prevent early exposure to drugs and alcohol among adolescents? Psychological Science, 19(10), 1037–1044. https://doi.org/10.1111/j.1467-9280.2008.02196.x

Overdose Detection Mapping Application Program. (2020). ODMAP. http://odmap.org/

Pan, K., & Wood, E. (2020). Bridging from harm reduction programs to evidence-based addiction treatment services. Canadian Journal of Addiction, 11(2), 24–26. https://doi.org/10.1097/CXA.0000000000000083

Parker, J. S. (2016). Brain maker: The power of gut microbes to heal and protect your brain–for life. The Yale Journal of Biology and Medicine, 89(3), 423. https://ncbi.nlm.nih.gov/pmc/articles/PMC5045150/

Podesta, A., & Hussey, J. E. (2019). Addressing/reducing the stigma of addictions across all professions [PowerPoint slides].

Poulose, S. M., Miller, M. G., Scott, T., & Shukitt-Hale, B. (2017). Nutritional factors affecting adult neurogenesis and cognitive function. Advances in Nutrition, 8(6), 804–811. https://doi.org/10.3945/an.117.016261

Sarlin, E. (2015, November 30). Long-term follow-up of medication-assisted treatment for addiction to pain relievers yields "cause for optimism." https://archives. drugabuse.gov/news-events/nida-notes/2015/11/long-term-follow-up-medication-assisted-treatment-addiction-to-pain-relievers-yields-cause-optimism

Shafiei, E., Hoseini, A. F., Bibak, A., & Azmal, M. (2014). High risk situations predicting relapse in self-referred addicts to bushehr province substance abuse treatment centers. International Journal of High Risk Behaviors & Addiction, 3(2), e16381. https://doi.org/10.5812/ijhrba.16381

Shatz, C. J. (1992). The developing brain. Scientific American, 267(3), 60–67. https://doi.org/10.1038/scientificamerican0992-60

Sleigh, J., Harvey, M., Voss, L., & Denny, B. (2014). Ketamine – More mechanisms of action than just NMDA blockade. Trends in Anaesthesia and Critical Care, 4(2), 76–81. https://doi.org/10.1016/j.tacc.2014.03.002

Smith, D. E. (2012). Editor's note: The process addictions and the new ASAM definition of addiction. Journal of Psychoactive Drugs, 44(1), 1–4. https://doi.org/10.1080/02791072.2012.662105

Sotres-Bayon, F., Cain, C. K., & LeDoux, J. E. (2006). Brain mechanisms of fear extinction: Historical perspectives on the contribution of prefrontal cortex. Biological Psychiatry, 60(4), 329–336. https://doi.org/10.1016/j.biopsych.2005.10.012

Sternat, T., & Katzman, M. A. (2016). Neurobiology of hedonic tone: The relationship between treatment-resistant depression, attention-deficit hyperactivity disorder, and substance abuse. Neuropsychiatric disease and treatment, 12, 2149–2164. https://doi.org/10.2147/NDT.S111818

Strang, J., Bearn, J., Farrell, M., Finch, E., Gossop, M., Griffiths, P., Marsden, J., & Wolff, K. (1998). Route of drug use and its implications for drug effect, risk of dependence and health consequences. Drug and Alcohol Review, 17(2), 197–211. https://doi.org/10.1080/09595239800187001

Substance Abuse and Mental Health Services Administration (SAMHSA). (2016, July 8). Medication assisted treatment for opioid use disorders. Federal Register. https://federalregister.gov/documents/2016/07/08/2016-16120/medication-assisted-treatment-for-opioid-use-disorders

Szalavitz, M. (2012, November 5). Hazelden introduces antiaddiction medications into recovery for first time: Recovery from opioid addiction may no longer mean complete abstinence from drugs. Time. https://healthland.time.

com/2012/11/05/hazelden-introduces-antiaddiction-medications-in-recovery-for-first-time/

Tadros, A., Sharon, M., Crum, M., Johnson, R., Quedado, K., & Fang, W. (2020). Coexistence of substance abuse among emergency department patients presenting with suicidal ideation. BioMed Research International, 2020. https://doi.org/10.1155/2020/7460701

The American College of Obstetricians and Gynecologists. (2015). Committee opinion no. 633: Alcohol abuse and other substance use disorders: Ethical issues in obstetric and gynecologic practice. Obstetrics & Gynecology, 125(6), 1529–1537. https://doi.org/10.1097/01.AOG.0000466371.86393.9b

Trivedi, M. H., Walker, R., Ling, W., dela Cruz, A., Sharma, G., Carmody, T., Ghitza, U. E., Wahle, A., Kim, M., Shores-Wilson, K., Sparenborg, S., Coffin, P., Schmitz, J., Wiest, K., Bart, G., Sonne, S. C., Wakhlu, S., Rush, A. J., Nunes, E. V., & Shoptaw, S. (2021). Bupropion and naltrexone in methamphetamine use disorder. New England Journal of Medicine, 384(2), 140–153. https://doi.org/10.1056/NEJMoa2020214

Womersley, J. S., & Uys, J. D. (2016). S-glutathionylation and redox protein signaling in drug addiction. Progress in Molecular Biology and Translational Science, 137, 87–121. https://doi.org/10.1016/bs.pmbts.2015.10.001

QUICK GUIDES AND RESOURCES

What to Ask a Rehab

- What is the cost?
- How much does insurance cover?
- Does the staff have expertise in treating my (child's, spouse's, friend's) addiction to (alcohol/benzodiazepines/opioids/cocaine/amphetamines/synthetics/cutting/sex/food/gambling/other)?
- Does the program provide individualized treatment planning?
- Is the facility based on 12-step/religion/a particular philosophy?
- Are there ancillary services, such as nutrition, massage, spiritual counseling? Are they included or additional?
- What types of counseling are provided?
- What is the typical length of stay?
- If the client or counselors recommend a longer length of stay, what is the cost?
- How is the family involved? Are there weekly family sessions available? Individual? Group? Is there a family weekend?
- Is there time set aside for clients who are professionals to work? To use the internet and phone? What other activities are available?
- Does the facility offer psychiatric consultation? Is addiction medication part of treatment? Medical treatment? Functional medicine? Nutrition?
- Is the medical director a physician, a therapist, a PhD, a nurse practitioner?

Find an Addiction Professional

Comprehensive treatment requires treating any and all pertinent parts of addiction. If you or a family member is looking to make a change in your life, and you do not already have a treatment provider, here are some resources to find a trained professional:

- Board Certified Addiction Physician Finder:
  https://certification.theabpm.org/physician-lookup
  https://www.aaap.org/education/resources/patients/
- Trained Addiction Counselors/Therapists:
  www.psychologytoday.com
  www.naadac.org/sap-directory
- Find a treatment provider that prescribes Medication Assisted Treatment:
  https://www.vivitrol.com/find-a-treatment-provider
  https://www.sublocade.com/
  https://www.samhsa.gov/medication-assisted-treatment/practitioner-program-data/treatment-practitioner-locator

Drugs Affecting Neurotransmitters

DRUG TYPE	SUBTYPE/FORM	NICKNAMES	RECEPTOR
Alcohol	Beer, wine, liquor	Juice, booze, sauce, hooch, suds, liquid courage	GABA/Glutamate
Cocaine	Powder cocaine, crack cocaine	Blow, bump, coke, crack, rock, snow	Dopamine
Stimulants	Street: Methamphetamine	Crystal, meth, ice, speed, crank, glass	Dopamine
	Prescribed: Amphetamine (Adderall, Benzedrine) Methylphenidate (Concerta, Ritalin, Vyvanse, Focalin, Daytrana)	Addy, smart drug, vitamin A, Vitamin R	

DRUG TYPE	SUBTYPE/FORM	NICKNAMES	RECEPTOR
Opioid/ Narcotic/Pain reliever	Street: Heroin	Brown sugar, China white, H, horse, smack, skag	Opioid
	Prescribed: Codeine, Hydrocodone, Lortab, Vicodin, Demerol, Methadone, Morphine, Oxycodone, Opana, Fentanyl	Cody, loads, China, Watson, footballs, demmies	
Cannabis	Marijuana, hashish	Blunt, bud, ganja, grass, weed, Mary Jane, trees	Cannabinoid
Ecstasy/ Molly	MDMA/MDA	X, XTC, E, Adam, roll	Serotonin
Inhalants	Paint thinner, lighter fluid, freeze spray, electronic cleaner, whipped cream aerosol containers, nitrous oxide, refrigerant gas	Whippets, nitrice, snappers, poppers, bolt, bullet	Most at NMDA; some asphyxiants
Synthetics	Synthetic cannabinoids	K2, spice, diablo, incense, black mamba, genie	Cannabinoid Dopamine, Norepinephrine, Serotonin
	Synthetic cathinones	Cloud9, vanilla sky, purple wave, bliss, blizzard, aura, MCAT	
Hallucinogens	Ketamine, LSD, mescaline, peyote, psilocybin, salvia, DMT, ayahuasca, PCP	Special K, acid, dots, cactus, love, mescal, shrooms, la purga	Most at Serotonin
Sedatives	Barbiturates: Phenobarbital, Pentobarbital	Barbs, reds, yellows	GABA
	Benzodiazepines: Xanax, Valium, Ativan, Klonopin	Zanbars, footballs, tranks, downers	
	Sleep Medications: Sonata, Ambien, Lunesta	Roofies, A minus, zombies	
Steroids	Testosterone, Anadrol, Oxandrin	Gym candy, juice, roids	GABA, Dopamine
Tobacco	Cigarettes, chewing tobacco, gum, patch	Smokes, chew	Nicotinic acetylcholine receptors, or nAChRs,

ABOUT THE AUTHOR

Arwen Podesta, MD, is a board-certified adult psychiatrist with sub-
specializations in addiction medicine,
forensic psychiatry, and integrative
medicine. A graduate of the University of Southern California Keck
School of Medicine, Dr. Podesta
completed her psychiatry residency
in at Louisiana State University before pursuing fellowship in Forensic
Psychiatry at Tulane University.

Following hurricane Katrina,
Dr Podesta worked to create greater
access to psychiatric care for under-
served and disenfranchised populations in the city. She has continued this
work in the public sector as Medical Director of multiple addiction treatment centers and as a consultant for the Orleans Criminal Court, Drug
Court and Re-entry Services. Additionally, she maintains status as a consulting Addiction Medicine Specialist and an expert witness.

Dr. Podesta maintains an active role in the academic community as
volunteer clinical faculty for several academic residencies and fellowships.
Her outstanding clinical and academic contributions to the field of medicine earned her a nomination for the role of President of the Louisiana
chapter of the American Society of Addiction Medicine in 2017. In
2019, she was awarded the honor of Distinguished Fellow of the American

Psychiatric Association. A renowned speaker, Dr. Podesta regularly travels to teach and speak on the topics of addiction medicine and integrative psychiatry.

Dr. Podesta has a boutique practice in New Orleans, where she collaborates with an excellent team, including psychotherapists, a nutritionist, massage therapists, and an acupuncturist. Podesta Wellness continues to evolve toward the multi-disciplinary collaborative model that embodies Dr. Podesta's wellness model for whole health.

CONTRIBUTORS

Elizabeth "Ellie" Richardson, MD, is a resident in psychiatry at the University of New Mexico. In her free time, she can be found exploring the New Mexican wilderness with her labradoodle and dancing to music. She enjoys hot Earl Grey tea, maple syrup, and pizza. Dr. Richardson is a lucky sister, daughter, friend, and granddaughter. Her interests include addiction psychiatry, child and adolescent psychiatry, and emergency psychiatry.

Ali Nakip, MD, MEd, CEDS, a psychiatry resident at the University of New Mexico, trained in and practiced medicine in Iraq before moving to the United States. He has an interest in eating disorders and addiction, is a certified eating disorders specialist, and is on the Food Addiction Institute's board of directors. He is a medical, academic, and technology integration consultant as well, which facilitates his work toward the improvement of the health-care delivery model. Dr. Nakip is married and has two children—a teenage boy and a daughter. He enjoys traveling and outdoor activities with his family.

ENDORSEMENTS FOR *HOOKED*

Hooked is the best kind of book–practical, pithy, and pointed. Dr. Podesta has delivered just what many people are looking for in a guide for true recovery from all types of addictions. This book will help many people who are now struggling find healing. I love it.

Scott Shannon, MD, ABIHM–
Past president of the American Board of Integrative Holistic Medicine

There is a pressing need right now for the kind of book that Dr. Podesta has produced, as our country struggles with a horrific opioid epidemic that takes thousands of lives each year. The science of addiction treatment has made significant advances in the last decade, so we now have the tools that we need to treat addiction effectively, but only when those treatments are in the hands of skilled practitioners. Dr. Podesta is a master clinician, and her book is a valuable primer that will benefit anybody who is struggling with an addiction or is working in the field.

Richard Juman, PsyD–
Editor, Professional Voices, TheFix.com

As an addiction psychiatrist, I'm always looking for readable books that I can recommend to people and their families that explain addiction in clear, simple, and accurate terms. In *Hooked*, Dr. Podesta covers all the basics–definitions, treatment approaches, lifestyle factors, and special issues like pain or pregnancy and addiction. I think it's extremely well written and a great read for anyone interested in the mechanics and treatment of addiction.

Omar Manejwala, MD–
Addiction psychiatrist, medical expert for media, and author

A well-organized biopsychosocial look at the principles of addiction in a digestible way. As useful as what works, *Hooked* also covers what does not.

Ken Knight, LPC–
Host, Therapy Evolved podcast

Dr. Podesta has written a wonderful, concise review that is meaningful to the clinician and layperson alike. As a practicing physician, I learned a great deal and appreciate the authoritative language and illustrative examples drawn from the author's own clinical practice. She covers types of substance abuse disorders, biological therapy, treatment options, and the role of supporting family and friends in precise, easy-to-understand language. Those with a loved one suffering from addiction will find particular value in this book. I highly recommend this book for any clinician caring for patients suffering from substance abuse disorders and for family and friends interested in a roadmap for the difficult task of providing the right type of support for a loved one.

Joe M. Kanter, MD, MPH–
Louisiana State Health Officer and Medical Director, New Orleans

Once I started reading *Hooked,* I couldn't put it down. It answered every question I've ever had about addiction and what to do about it.

With hundreds of books and many different (and often conflicting) theories on addiction it can be confusing and overwhelming to try to decide what path to take for treatment.

Finally, a no-blame, no-shame book that offers the most current information that makes sense.

As a therapist and an expert in the field at the biological basis of personality, I was very impressed with the science presented in this book. I recommend it to all of my clients who have an addiction or have a loved one, friend, or colleague who does. So far, every one of them has found *Hooked* to be straightforward and easy to understand and utilize.

Thank you, Dr. Podesta, for creating a seminal piece of work that can help laypeople and professionals in the field understand the dynamics of addiction and what to do about it.

Tina Thomas, PhD, LCSW, BSN–
Clinical social work/therapist

The book *Hooked* is consistent with Dr. Podesta's early work post-Katrina navigating the emergency mental health and correctional systems, plus the web of homeless support efforts. This comprehensive book is especially useful for families dealing with the opioid crisis, homelessness, and disconnected dual-diagnosis residents, and prepping them to collaborate with our local first-responders and health and mental health stakeholder agencies. Page 65 goes deeper into "relapse" and "trust" than I've ever seen.

Les Holcomb, MPH–
Community activist and patient advocate in Duke County, Massachusetts

Hooked is an information-packed treatise on substance abuse. It covers the important factors contributing to the development of substance abuse and is filled with practical advice. *Hooked* includes an up-to-date look at medical and therapy treatments. Yet it also reviews promising, safe, and often-overlooked approaches to treat the whole person such as with nutritional interventions.

Motivated patients in action phase will benefit from this book, as will professionals and families. Highly recommended.

Kristopher Kaliebe, MD–
Associate professor of psychiatry at the University of South Florida in Tampa

INDEX

N

O

P

R

CPSIA information can be obtained
at www.ICGtesting.com
Printed in the USA
LVHW081441191221
706618LV00003B/63

9 781952 481314